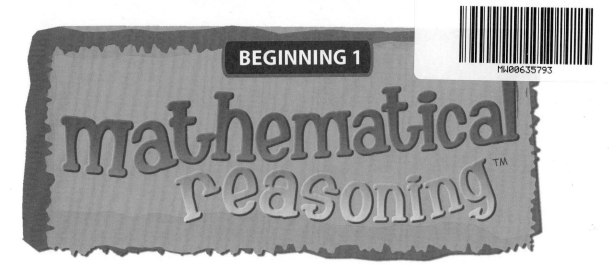

BEGINNING 1

Mathematical Reasoning™ products available in print or eBook form.

Beginning 1 • Beginning 2
Level A • Level B • Level C • Level D • Level E
Level F • Level G • Understanding Pre-Algebra
Understanding Geometry • Understanding Algebra I
Grades 2-4 Supplement • Grades 4-6 Supplement
Middle School Supplement (Grades 7-9)

Written by
Linda Brumbaugh and Doug Brumbaugh

Graphic Design by
Karla Garrett ▪ Trisha Dreyer
Doug Brumbaugh ▪ Annette Langenstein

© 2009
THE CRITICAL THINKING CO.™
(Bright Minds™)
www.CriticalThinking.com
Phone: 800-458-4849 • Fax: 541-756-1758
1991 Sherman Ave., Suite 200 • North Bend • OR 97459
ISBN 978-0-89455-886-3

ABOUT THE AUTHORS

Linda S. Brumbaugh

I retired after teaching a total of 31 years in grades three, four, and five. Both my BS from the University of Florida and Masters from the University of Central Florida are in Elementary Education. As I look back over my teaching career, I enjoyed seeing the excitement on the children's faces as they encountered new concepts, worked with a manipulative, experienced some new mathematical application, or played a new mathematical game. It was stimulating when they solved an intricate problem, discovered something new to them, or got caught up in some new mathematical trick. As they got excited about learning, so did I. Each day of every year brought some new learning opportunity for me and for the children. I continue to work with pre-school and elementary age children in the Sunday school system of our church. Our intent is to convey some of that excitement to each child who uses this book.

Douglas K. Brumbaugh

Depending on how you count, I have been teaching for more than 50 years. I taught in college, in-service, or K-20 almost daily. I received my BS from Adrian College, and Masters and Doctorate in Mathematics Education from the University of Georgia. Students change, classroom environments change, the curriculum changes, and I change. The thoughts and examples used here are based on my teaching experiences over the years. These pages in this book are designed to spark the interest of each child who works with them.

TABLE OF CONTENTS

NCTM Standards

Skills	Number and Operations	Algebra	Geometry	Measurement	Data Analysis and Probability
Count	1, 2, 3, 4, 5, 7, 8, 9, 10, 11, 14, 17, 18, 19, 23, 26, 29, 31, 36, 69, 74, 86, 96, 97, 99, 117, 129, 131, 135, 144, 148, 155, 175, 183, 197	6, 83, 113, 184	21, 22, 25, 26, 104, 118, 194, 195, 206		12, 13, 28, 30, 32, 35, 41, 44, 48, 50, 51, 52, 55, 56, 59, 77, 152, 174, 176
Fractions	228, 229		202		
Language	54, 60, 66, 84, 85, 89, 106, 107, 140, 141, 145, 146, 178, 204	47, 53	38, 108, 112, 122, 133, 147, 209, 230	39, 61, 70, 72, 78, 79, 80, 81, 98, 100, 109, 114, 127, 137, 161, 165, 181, 182, 218, 223	67, 75, 76, 88, 91, 95, 124, 149, 157, 184, 211, 220
Manipulative			215		235
Match	37, 42, 138, 139, 142, 147, 151, 179	63, 169	43, 46, 62		34, 57, 71, 73, 82, 93, 104, 130, 132, 143, 153, 173, 212, 221
Order	102, 154, 156, 163, 170, 201		207	116, 200, 202, 219	68, 87, 115, 126, 216
Pattern	92, 134	20, 65, 101, 103, 105, 110, 128, 136, 168, 171, 192, 203, 208			94, 162
Shape	90, 189, 190, 210	45, 49, 112	15, 16, 24, 27, 33, 40, 58, 111, 119, 120, 121, 123, 147, 158, 159, 160, 164, 166, 167, 172, 177, 185, 193, 196, 222, 223, 233		125, 191, 198, 205, 232
Subtraction	213, 214, 217, 227, 236			224, 225, 226	186, 187, 188

About This Book

Teaching and practicing preschool math concepts and skills has never been easier! This unique all-in-one book allows parents to learn right along with their child—no lesson preparation needed! This will save you hours of time. Each section introduces a specific topic, followed by appropriate practice and application activities. The activities in this book are written to the standards of the National Council of Teachers of Mathematics (NCTM). Children enjoy the colorful, engaging challenges of the varying activities!

How to Use This Book

This book focuses on numbers 1-5. *Mathematical Reasoning® Beginning 2* focuses on the numbers 0-10. The skills and concepts presented in both books spiral throughout each book. That means that you will see a topic dealt with for a few pages and then a gap before it is covered again. We do that so your child has some time to develop and mature before dealing with more complex aspects of the skill/concept.

Our suggestion is that you proceed through this book page by page. A child who successfully finishes *Mathematical Reasoning® Beginning 1 and 2* will know and be able to apply the mathematics skills and concepts taught to most kindergartners.

Please note: Most 3-year-olds can be taught to add, subtract, and reason mathematically, but just as all children do not grow at the same rate, not all brains develop at the same rate. If your child struggles, don't be alarmed and jump to conclusions about your child's intelligence. If your child has trouble identifying shapes, colors, or the concept of sets (groups), we suggest working with your child in *Building Thinking Skills® Beginning 1* before or concurrently with this book.

Teaching Suggestions

Keep learning fun and avoid frustrating your child. Work around your child's attention span. As a parent, you have a great advantage to teach young children because most young children love to spend time with Mom and Dad. If you keep learning fun, you will have an energetic pupil who looks forward to each and every lesson.

Using Concrete Objects: If your child struggles with an activity, you can come back to it later or try recreating the activity using objects your child can touch and feel (e.g. little blocks or counting bears). There is no one correct way to teach the skills taught in this book. Have fun figuring out different ways to repeat the skills taught in this book within your child's daily life.

Touch & Say (Count)

1

1   2

1   2   3

Touch & Say (Count)

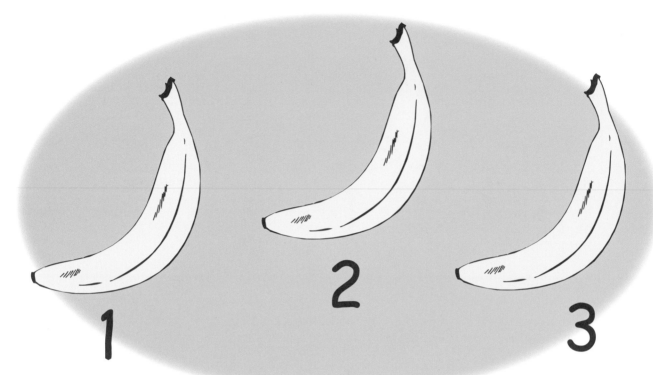

1   2   3

1   2

Count aloud the number of animals in each picture.

Count aloud the number of animals in each picture.

2

1

2

3

2

1

Count aloud the number of animals in each picture.

2

3

2

1

3

1

How many balloons?
Color 1 of the balloons.

How many pigs?
Color 2 of the pigs.

 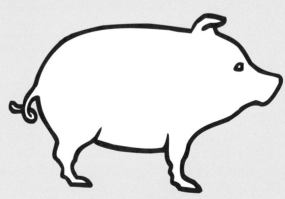

Teaching Note: Encourage your child to color within the lines.

How many moons?
Color 1 of the moons.

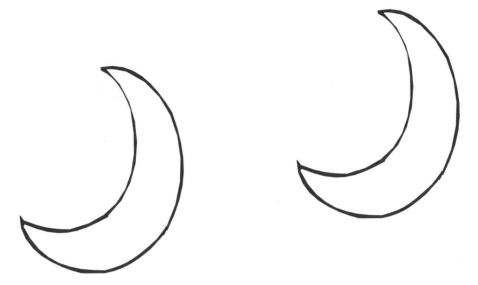

How many chickens?
Color 2 of the chickens.

Teaching Note: Encourage your child to color within the lines.

Count aloud the number of animals in each picture.

Count aloud the number of animals in each picture.

How many hearts?
Color 1 of the hearts.

How many bears?
Color 2 of the bears.

Teaching Note: Encourage your child to color within the lines.

1. Which picture has one dog?

2. Which picture has three dogs?

3. Which picture has two dogs?

4. Which picture has the fewest dogs?

5. Which picture has the most dogs?

1. Which picture has two apples?

2. Which picture has three apples?

3. Which picture has one apple?

4. Which picture has the most apples?

5. Which picture has the fewest apples?

Count aloud, then point to the correct numeral.

1 2 3 4 5

1. How many children are in the picture?

2. How many balloons are in the picture?

3. Draw three strings so each child has a balloon.

This is a circle. Trace the shape of the circle with your finger.

How many red circles are in each picture?

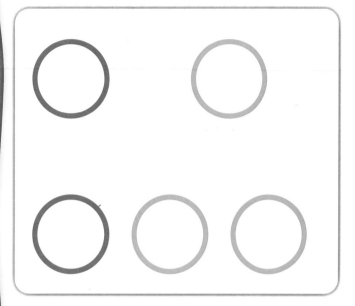

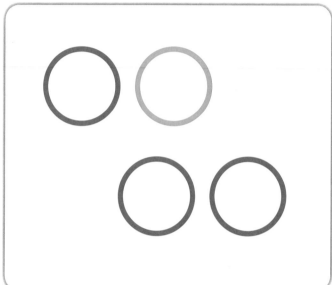

How many blue circles are in each picture?

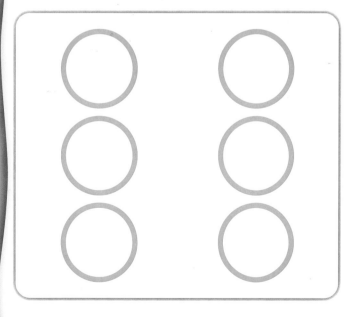

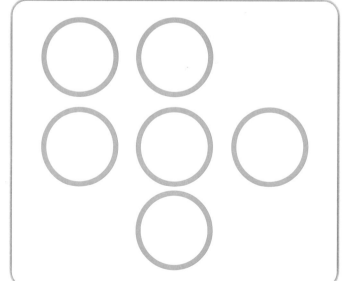

This is a
straight line

This is a
curved line

This is a
straight line

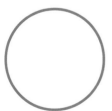

This is a
curved line

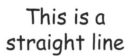

This is a
straight line

This is a
curved line

Is this line
straight or
curved?

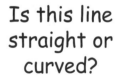

Is this line
straight or
curved?

Is this line
straight or
curved?

Is this line
straight or
curved?

Is this line
straight or
curved?

Is this line
straight or
curved?

Is this line
straight or
curved?

Is this line
straight or
curved?

Is this line
straight or
curved?

Corners are made when straight line segments meet.

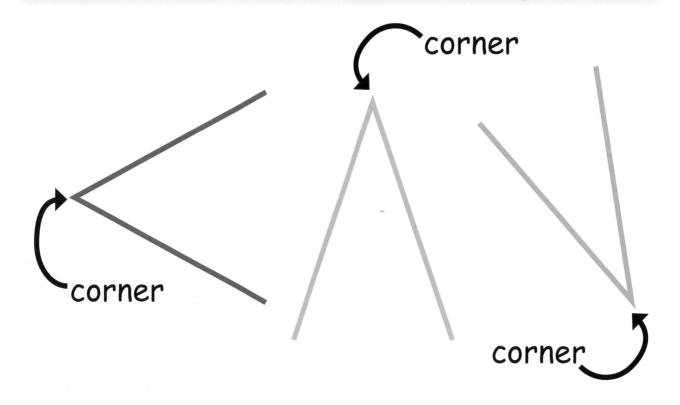

corner

corner

corner

How many corners does this shape have?

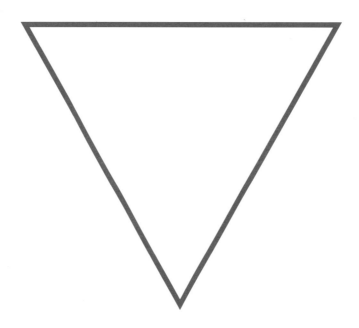

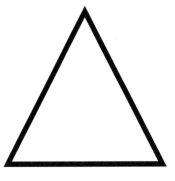 This is a triangle. It has 3 straight sides and 3 corners.

Count the sides.
Count the corners.

How many green triangles are in each picture?

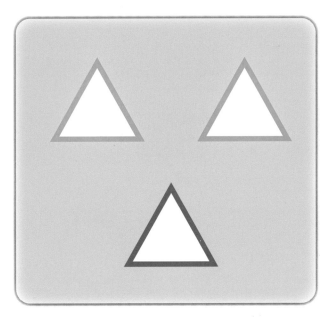

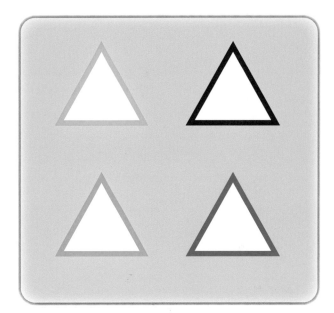

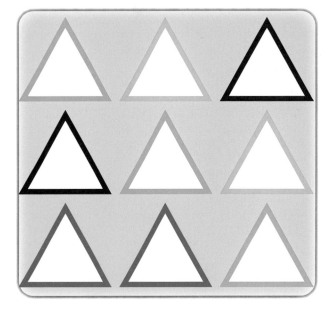

Point to each picture with two red circles.

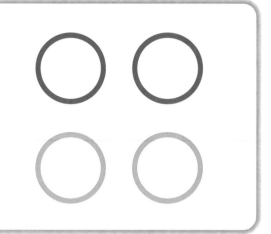

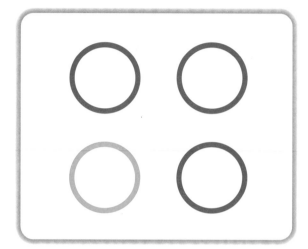

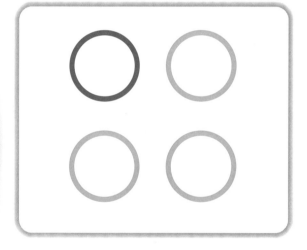

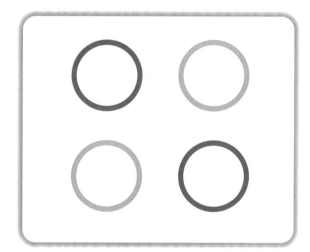

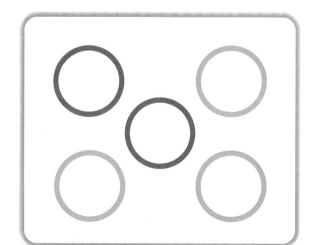

Point to each picture with three blue circles.

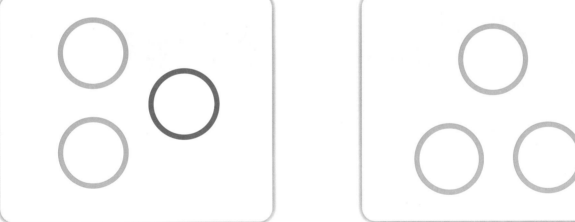

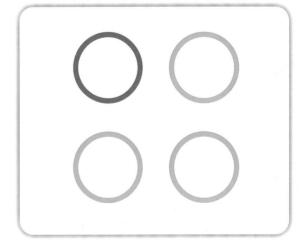

Touch and say the name of each object in the pattern. Then say the name of the object behind the yellow curtain that will continue the pattern.

This is a rectangle.
It has 4 straight sides and 4 corners.

Count the sides.
Count the corners.

How many red rectangles are in each picture?

How many triangles?
Color 1 of the triangles.

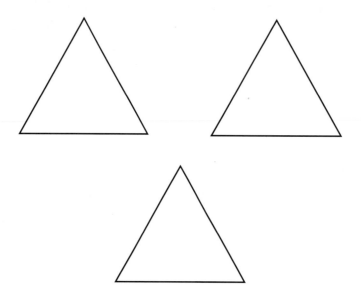

How many rectangles?
Color 2 of the rectangles.

Teaching Note: Encourage your child to color within the lines.

CAN YOU FIND ME?*

One kitten has five.

Another has more.

I have fewer,

but I don't have four.

Of the kittens you can see,

tell me now, can you find me?

*For more activities like this, see our *Can You Find Me?*™ series.

Squares are special rectangles.
The sides of squares are all the same.

This is a square.

This is not a square.

This is a square.

This is not a square.

Is this is a square?

Is this is a square?

Is this is a square?

Is this is a square?

Is this is a square?

Is this is a square?

How many black squares are in each picture?

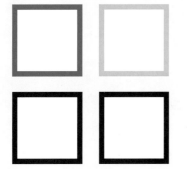

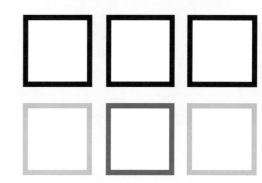

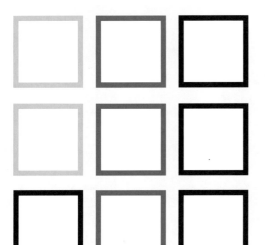

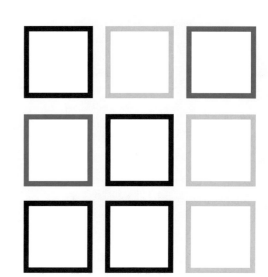

Point to each picture with two red squares.

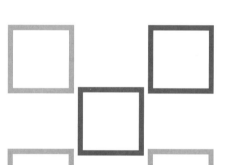

1. Point to the yellow object and say its shape.
2. Point to the black object and say its shape.
3. Point to the blue object and say its shape.
4. Point to the red object and say its shape.

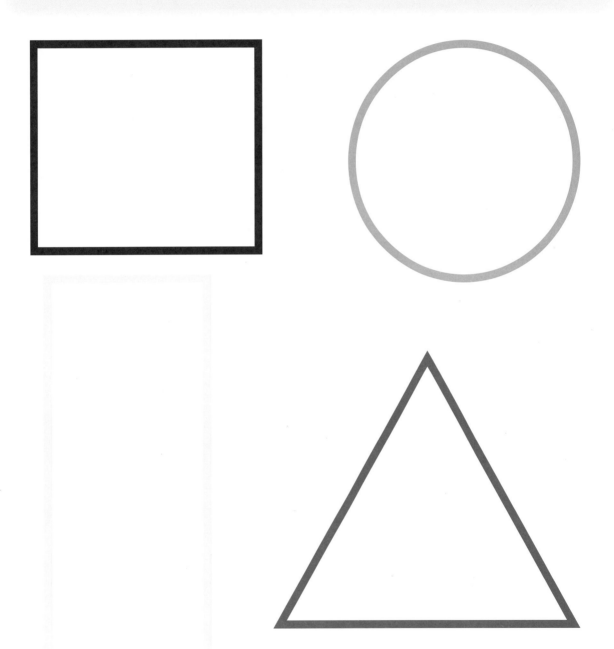

Teaching Note: A square is both a rectangle and a square. If your child calls a square a rectangle, ask him what type of rectangle.

1. Point to the picture with one fish.

2. Point to the picture with two fish.

3. Point to the picture with three fish.

4. Which picture has the fewest fish?

5. Which picture has the most fish?

1. Point and count how many red cars.

2. Point and count how many blue cars.

3. How many cars are in the picture?

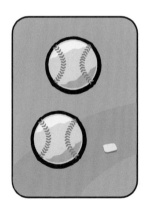

1. Point and count how many soccer balls.

2. Point and count how many baseballs.

3. How many balls are in both pictures?

Point to the picture that matches the description.

- two yellow ducks
- three red chickens
- three blue chickens
- two yellow chickens

CAN YOU FIND ME?*

I am shiny, I am new.

Of my color, you'll count two.

I am not old, nor colored gold,

Those are the clues I have for you.

Of the four pictures that you see,

tell me now, can you find me?

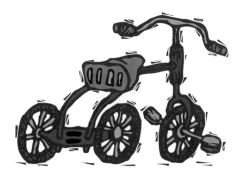

*For more activities like this, see our *Can You Find Me?*™ series.

Point to the picture that matches the description.

- three green squares
- four blue circles
- two red horses
- three red horses

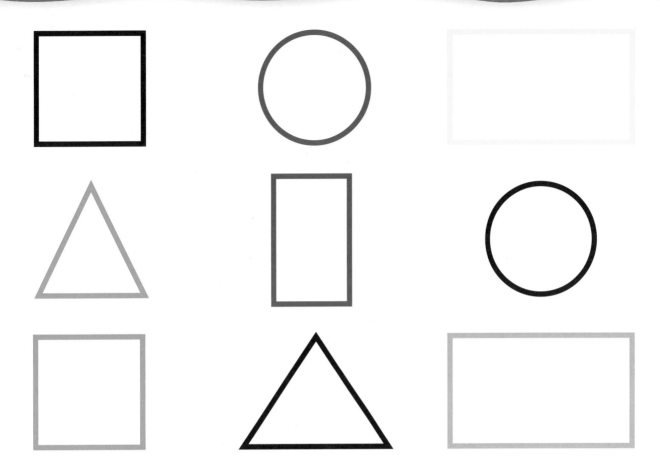

Point to the shape I describe.

- the black triangle

- the black circle

- the green square

- the red rectangle

- the green triangle

- the blue rectangle

- the black square

- the red circle

- the yellow rectangle

1. How many boys are in the picture?

2. How many balloons are in the picture?

3. Draw a line segment from each balloon to the boy with the same colored shirt.

4. Now, are all the balloons connected to a boy?

5. Which boy has more balloons?

6. Which boy has fewer balloons?

Point to the picture that matches the description.

- four red roosters
- four yellow sheep
- three blue fish
- four yellow horses

Use your fingers on one hand to count the number of animals in each picture.

3
horses

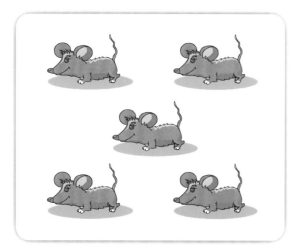

Draw line segments to connect the matching quantities.

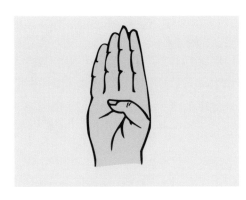

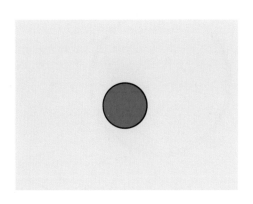

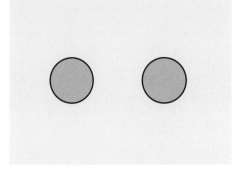

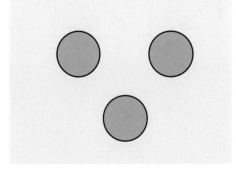

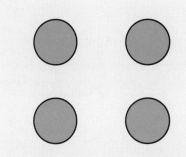

Point to the shape that matches each description.

- red circle
- green circle
- blue star
- blue square
- blue circle

- green triangle
- red star
- red triangle
- yellow square

Which crayon is longer?
Which crayon is shorter?

Which train is longer?
Which train is shorter?

Point to the shape that matches each description.

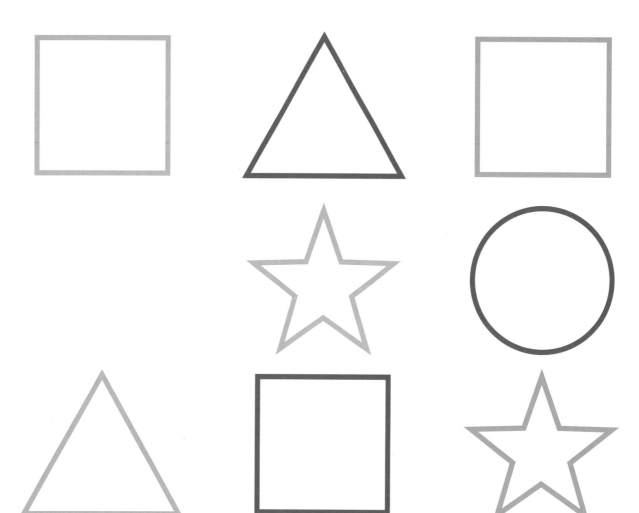

- blue star
- yellow circle
- red circle
- green square
- blue square

- red triangle
- green star
- blue triangle
- red square

1. Point and count how many sharks.

2. Point and count how many swordfish.

3. How many fish are in the pictures?

1. Point and count how many blue houses.

2. Point and count how many yellow houses.

3. How many houses are in the picture?

CAN YOU FIND ME?*

I'm less than five,

but you'll need another clue.

Point to me below,

I'm more than two.

Of the numbers you can see,

tell me now, can you find me?

*For more activities™ like this, see our *Can You Find Me?*™ series.

Point to the shape that matches each description.

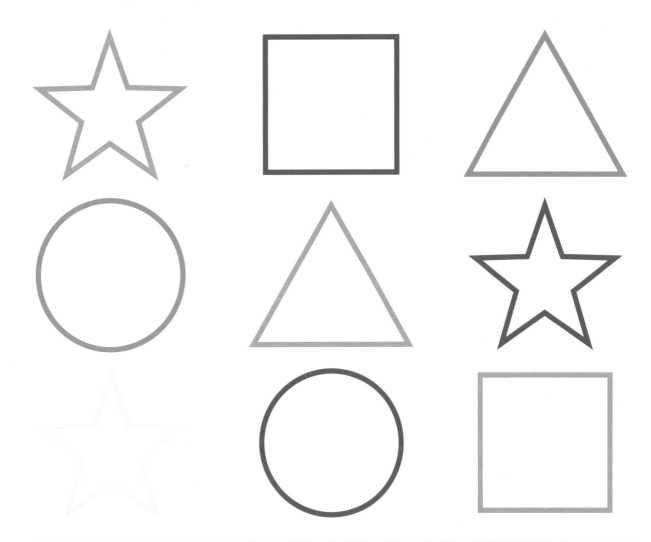

- blue square
- red star
- red circle
- green circle
- yellow star

- green triangle
- blue triangle
- blue star
- red square

Use your fingers on one hand to count the number of each animal.

- How many cows?   - How many horses?

- How many pigs?   - How many ducks?

- How many chickens?   - How many fish?

Point to the shape each car will find at the end of its road.

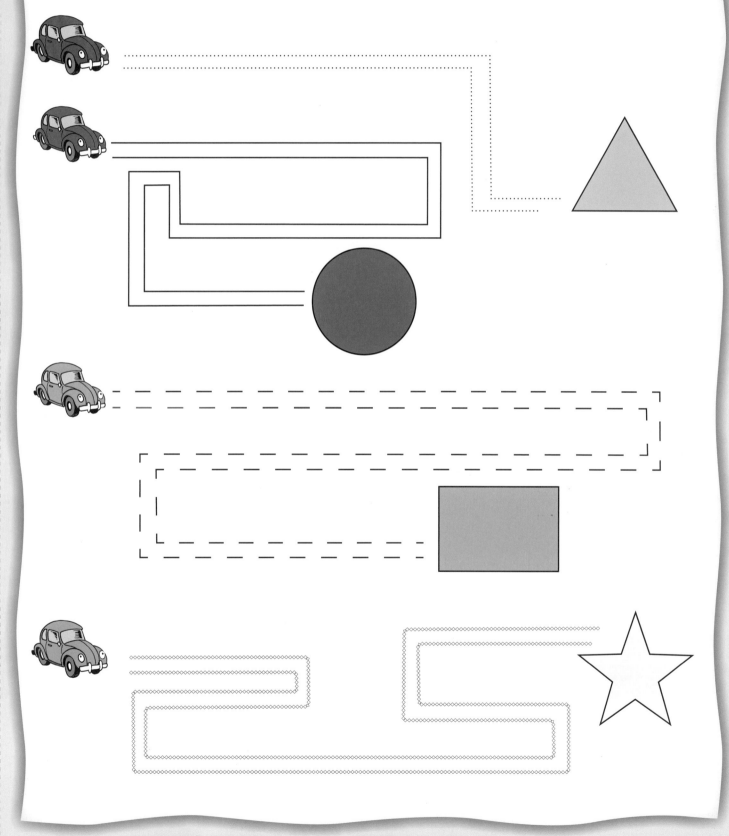

Draw line segments to connect the same shapes in each group.

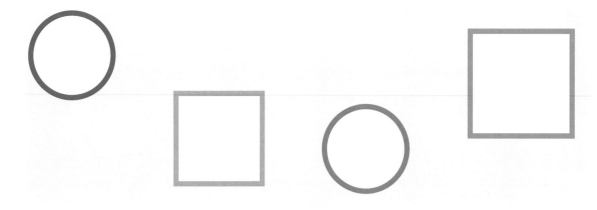

Point to the picture that matches the description.

- two red butterflies
- three blue boats
- four green frogs

- one blue boat
- three red butterflies
- two green frogs

1. How many toys are beside the girl?

2. How many toys are in front of the girl?

3. Are there more toys beside or in front of the girl?

4. If two more toys were moved beside the girl, would there be more toys in front of or beside her?

Draw line segments to connect the same shapes in each group.

Touch and count aloud the fruits in each picture.

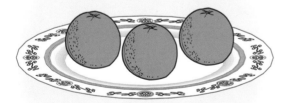
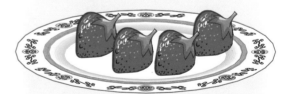

How many pigs are in the picture?
How many chicks are in the picture?

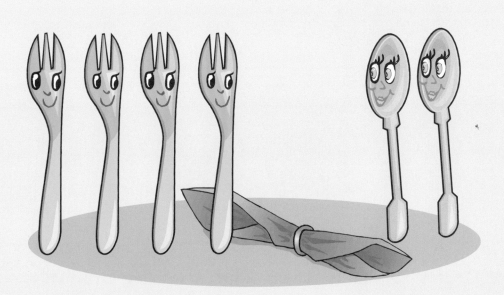

How many forks are in the picture?
How many spoons are in the picture?

How many red balls is the clown holding?
How many blue balls is the clown holding?
How many balls altogether are in the picture?

How many birdhouses are in the picture?
How many doghouses are in the picture?
How many houses altogether are in the picture?

1. Touch each ball and say its color.

2. Which ball is the largest?

3. Which ball is the smallest?

4. Which ball is the middle size?

1.   How many airplanes are on the ground?
2.   How many airplanes are flying?
3.   How many airplanes altogether?

1.   How many cupcakes have a candle?
2.   How many cupcakes have no candles?
3.   How many cupcakes altogether?

1. Point to the group of blocks with two blocks.

2. Point to the group of blocks with three blocks.

3. Point to the group of blocks with the fewest blocks.

4. Point to the group of blocks with the most blocks.

Point to the groups that have 2.
Point to the groups that have 3.

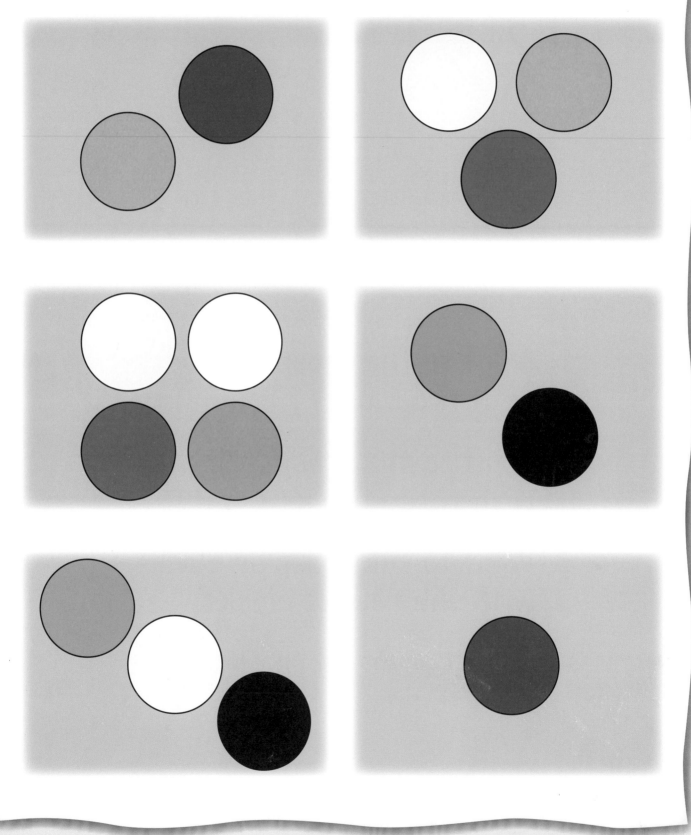

CAN YOU FIND ME?*

Three goats at a feast,

the largest goat ate the least.

The smallest goat ate the most,

he even ate all the toast.

That was them, it wasn't me,

which of these goats must I be?

Of these three goats that you see,

tell me now, can you find me?

*For more activities like this, see our *Can You Find Me?*™ series.

Say the color and shape of each figure.

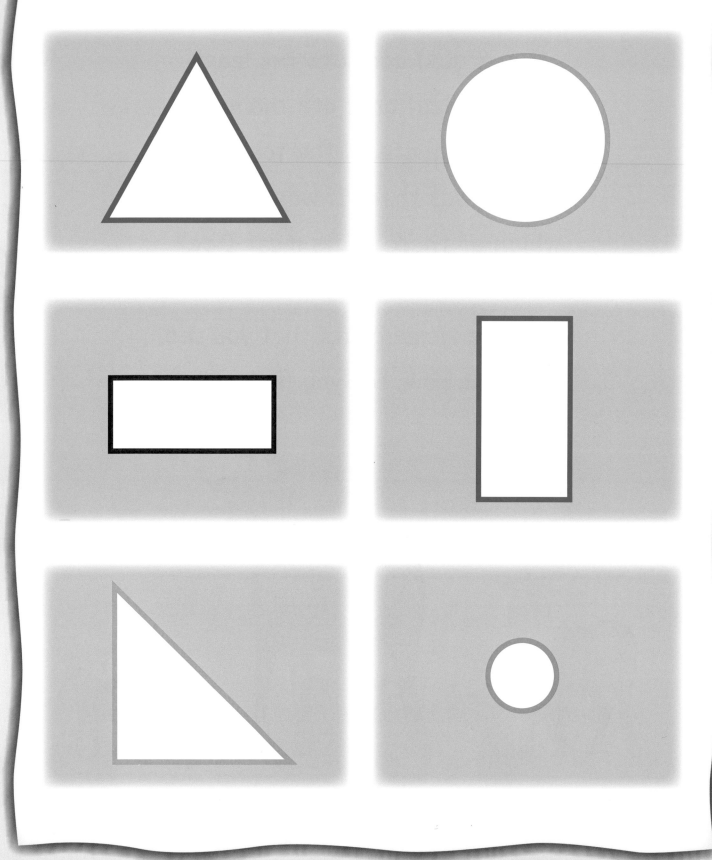

How many yellow pencils are in the picture?

How many red pencils are in the picture?

How many blue pencils are in the picture?

How many pencils altogether in the picture?

Which cookie is the biggest?

Which cookie is the smallest?

Which cookie is not the biggest or the smallest?

How many caps?
Color 3 of them.

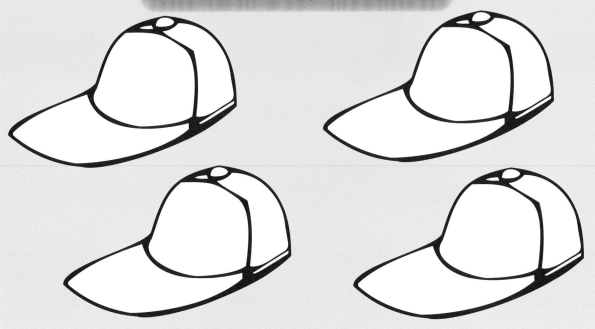

How many circles?
Color 3 of them.

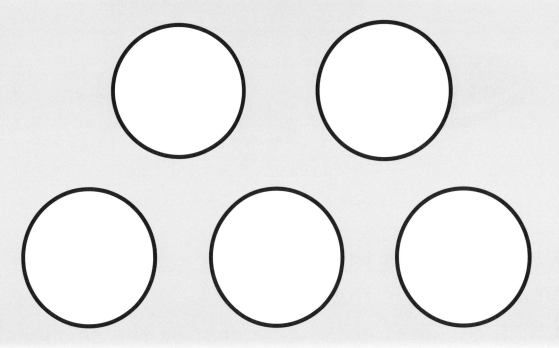

Teaching Note: Encourage your child to color within the lines.

1. Which fish is the longest?

2. Which fish is the shortest?

3. Which two fish are shorter?

Draw a line segment from each numeral to the matching number of dots.

     1   

   **2**   

   **3**

Draw line segments to connect the same shapes in each picture.

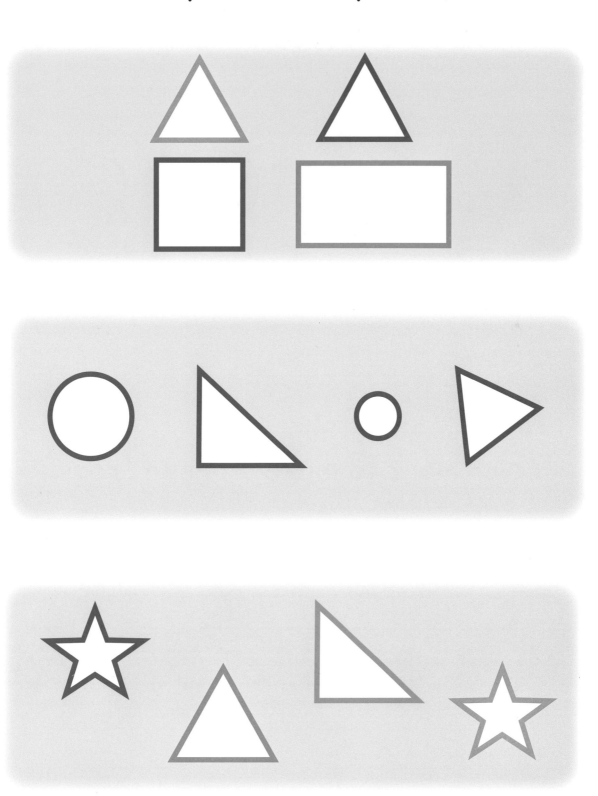

How many apples are red?
Color more to make 3 red apples.

How many frogs are green?
Color more to make 3 green frogs.

Touch and say the name of each item in the pattern. Then say the name of the object behind the green curtain that will continue the pattern.

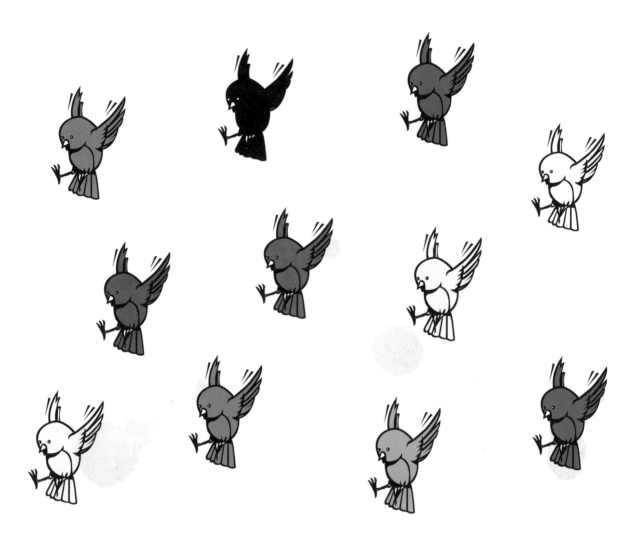

Count the red birds on the page.

Count the yellow birds on the page.

Count the blue birds on the page.

1. How many children are in the picture?

2. How many clouds are in the picture?

3. Are there more children or clouds?

1.   Point to the animal winning the race.
     The animal winning the race is first.

2.   Point to the animal losing the race.
     The animal losing the race is third.

3.   Point to the animal that is first in
     the race.

4.   Point to the animal that is second in
     the race.

5.   Point to the animal that is third in the race.

Use your fingers on one hand to count the number of things in each picture.

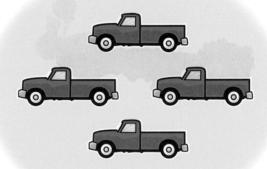

The dog is at the top of the stairs.

The girl is at the bottom of stairs.

Say Top or Bottom to tell each location.

Is the bird at the

Top or **Bottom**

of the ladder?

Is the candle in the

Top or **Bottom**

of the cake?

Top or Bottom?

Top or Bottom?

Point to each picture that has two things in it.

Say Top or Bottom to tell each location.

Top or Bottom?

Top or Bottom?

Top or Bottom?

Top or Bottom?

CAN YOU FIND ME?*

Near the bottom at the base,

my dustpan friend wears an unhappy face.

I have bristles, I am not a mop.

Look at my smile, I've made it to the top.

Of the four pictures that you see,

tell me now, can you find me?

*For more activities like this, see our *Can You Find Me?*™ series.

Use your fingers on one hand to count the number of fish in each picture.

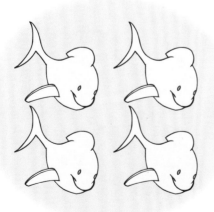

Which dog has more spots?
Which dog has fewer spots?

Which penguin has fewer fish?
Which penguin has more fish?

Which jar has more gum balls?
Which jar has fewer gum balls?

Which jar has fewer candies?
Which jar has more candies?

Point to the picture that matches the description.

- The toys are in front of the girl.
- The toys are in back of the girl.
- The toys are beside the girl.

Which child is taller?
Which child is shorter?

Which building is taller?
Which building is shorter?

Which tree is the tallest?

Which tree is the shortest?

Which tree is not the shortest <u>or</u> the tallest?

Which person is the shortest?

Which person is the tallest?

Which person is not the shortest <u>or</u> the tallest?

Which truck is longer?
Which truck is shorter?

Which caterpillar is longer?
Which caterpillar is shorter?

Which worm is the longest?

Which worm is the shortest?

Which worm is not the longest <u>or</u> the shortest?

Which pencil is the shortest?

Which pencil is not the shortest <u>or</u> the longest?

Which pencil is the longest?

CAN YOU FIND ME?*

I'm playing in a high tree fort.

The rope to the ground is too short.

I'm not climbing down this tree,

because it might be the end of me.

Of the pictures that you can see,

tell me now, can you find me?

*For more activities like this, see our *Can You Find Me?*™ series.

Touch and count each side of each triangle.

How many straight sides are in a triangle?

Count aloud, then point to the correct number.

1 2 3 4 5

How many orange fish?

How many green fish?

How many fish in all?

Count aloud, then point to the correct number.

How many blue crayons?

How many green crayons?

How many crayons altogether?

1 2 3 4 5

How many black crayons?

How many red crayons?

How many crayons altogether?

Point to each picture and tell how many trucks or dogs.

Point to the correct answer.

Who will be the first one in the water?

Who will be the second one in the water?

Who will be the fourth one in the water?

Who will be the third one in the water?

Who is the tallest?

Who is the shortest?

Who is the 2nd tallest?

Who is the 2nd shortest?

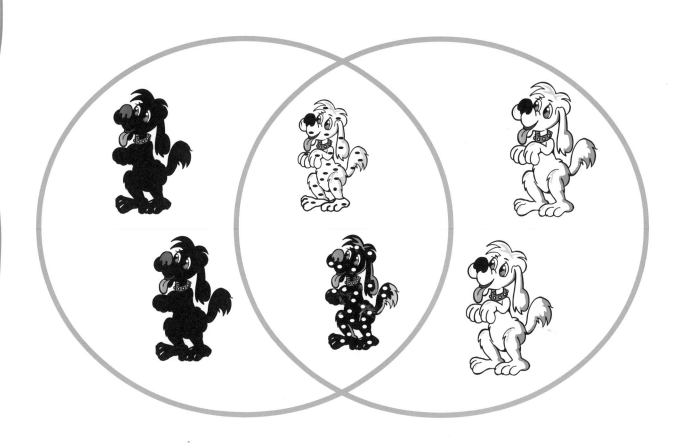

1. How many dogs are all black?

2. How many dogs are all white?

3. How many dogs are both black and white?

Count aloud, then point to the number of things in each picture.

1 2 3 4 5

1 tent

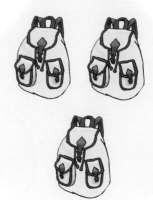

How many circles?
Color 2 of them.

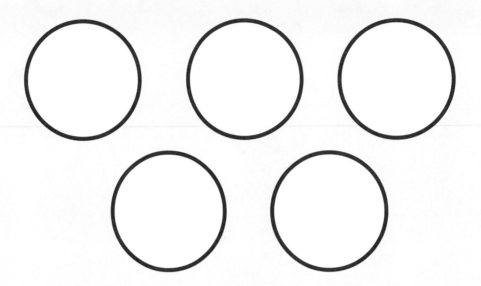

How many triangles?
Color 4 of them.

1. Point to the picture that has one butterfly.

2. Point to the picture that has two butterflies.

3. Point to the picture that has three butterflies.

4. Point to the picture that has the fewest butterflies.

5. Point to the picture that has the most butterflies.

6. Point to the picture with the biggest butterfly.

7. Point to the picture with the smallest butterfly.

Point to each group with 3, then point to each group with 4.

Count aloud, then point to the correct number.

1 2 3 4 5

1. How many children are in the picture?

2. How many tricycles are in the picture?

3. We can show that there is the same number of things in groups by connecting things in one group with things in the other group. Draw a line segment to connect each tricycle with a child.

Point to each group with 4 fish.
Point to each group with 2 fish.

3/15/23

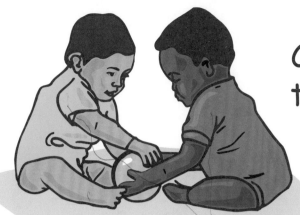

Count aloud, then point to the correct number.

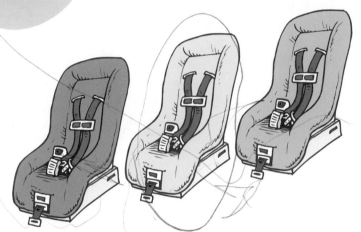

1 2 3 4 5

We can show that there is the same number of things in groups by connecting things in one group with things in the other group.

1. How many children are in the top picture?

2. How many car seats are in the bottom picture?

3. Draw a line segment to connect each child with a car seat.

4. How many car seats are not connected to a child?

3/15/23

How many trees?
Color 3 trees.

How many balloons?
Color 4 balloons.

3/20/23

Point to the pictures that have three things in them.

Teaching note: If your child is determining the set of three by counting, offer praise. It is important that children recognize "threeness" when the objects are in different arrangements. As your child moves about the room, house, yard, or play area, ask for examples of three things.

Say Top or Bottom to tell each location.

Top or **Bottom?**

Top or Bottom?

Top or Bottom?

Top or Bottom?

3/20/23

Point to the pictures that have four things in them.
Say how you can tell the pictures have four things in them.

Teaching note: If your child is determining the set of four by counting, offer praise. It is important that children recognize "fourness" when the objects are in different arrangements. As your child moves about the room, house, yard, or play area, ask for examples of four things.

3/23/23

Which glass has the least orange juice?
Which glass has the most orange juice?

Which cloud has the most raindrops?
Which cloud has fewest raindrops?

3/23/23

Touch and say the name of each item in the pattern. Then say the name of the object behind the green curtain that will continue the pattern.

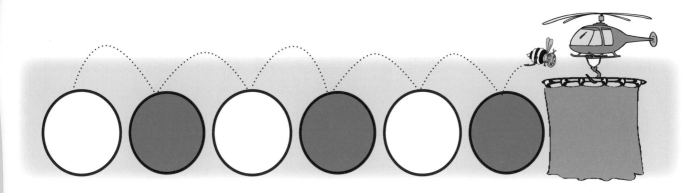

3/23/23

zeb did great!

Point to the child who is first in line and say the color of his shirt.

Point to the child who is second in line and say the color of her shirt.

Teaching Note: Similar situations could be established with toys and acted out with your child. As your child is traveling, comment about which car is first at a traffic light, which bicycle and rider is first or second in line or at sport practice, who will be going first and second.

Good Job! 🙂

Touch and say the name of each item in the pattern. Then say the name of the object behind the green curtain that will continue the pattern.

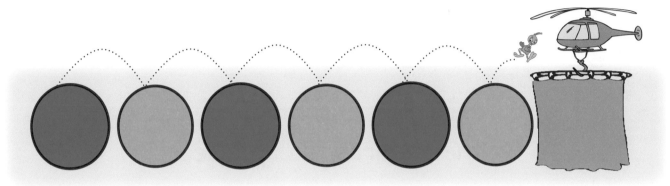

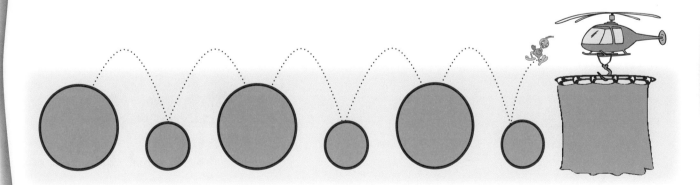

CAN YOU FIND ME?*

We look like a green parade.

From tiny seeds, we were made.

In the sun, we look fine.

All four of us in a line.

Of the pictures that you see,

which one must this group be?

*For more activities like this, see our *Can You Find Me?*™ series.

Touch and say the name of each item in the pattern. Then say the name of the object behind the green curtain that will continue the pattern.

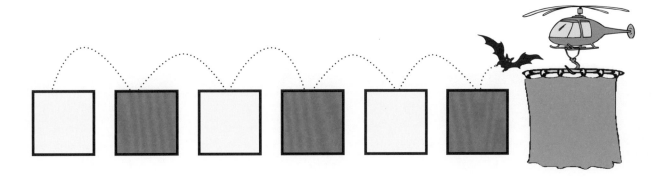

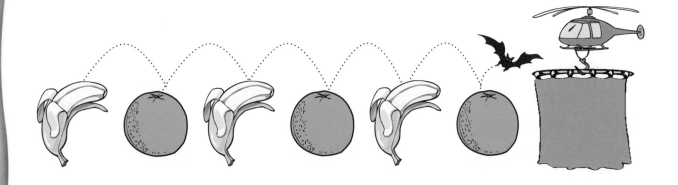

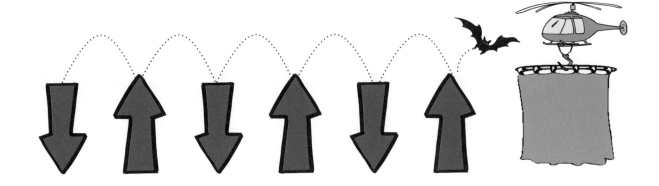

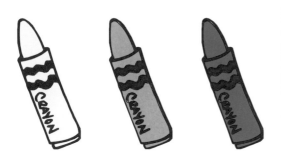

1. How many yellow crayons are there in the picture?
2. How many red crayons are there in the picture?
3. How many blue crayons are there in the picture?
4. How many crayons are there in the picture?

1. Point to a button on the clown's shirt and say its color.
2. Point to a different color button on the clown's shirt and say its color.
3. Point to another different color button on the clown's shirt and tell me its color.
4. How many buttons in the picture?
5. If one button falls off, how many buttons are left?

Teaching note: These activities provide the background for subtraction. This is a difficult process for many children to understand and you might need to delay the exposure for your child until later in the year.

1. Which candy cane is the tallest?
2. Which candy cane is the shortest?
3. Which candy cane is the middle-sized one?
4. Draw a candy cane bigger than the biggest candy cane.

Touch and count the corners of each triangle.

How many corners are in every triangle?

Take 1 giant step.

Take 2 regular steps.

Take 3 tiny steps.

Take 4 bunny hops.

Teaching Note: Some people play the game using the rule that the player must say "May I" before making any move. Play this game with a few children, varying the directions as appropriate.

Touch and say the name of each item in the pattern. Then say the name of the object behind the green curtain that will continue the pattern.

CAN YOU FIND ME?*

I have three sides, my lines are straight

but, to find me, you must wait.

Count my corners 1, 2, 3.

These three clues lead you to me.

Of the four pictures that you see,

tell me now, can you find me?

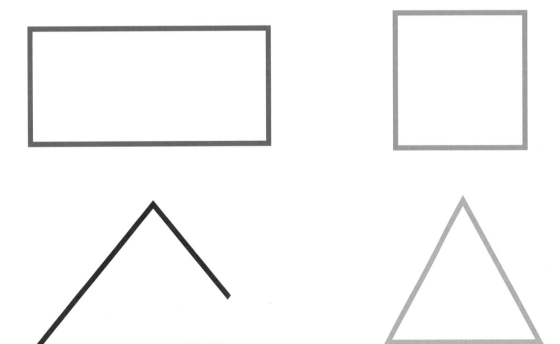

*For more activities like this, see our *Can You Find Me?*™ series.

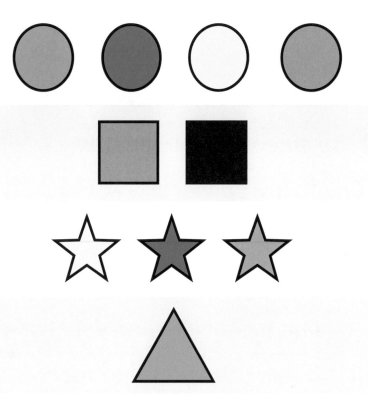

Name each type of shape in the box.

How many circles are there?

How many squares are there?

How many stars are there?

Are there more stars or squares?

Are there more circles or stars?

Use the fingers on one hand to show the number of ducks in each picture.

1.　Point to the longest line segment.

2.　Point to the shortest line segment.

3.　Draw a line that is longer than all of these line segments.

4.　Draw a line that is shorter than all of these line segments.

4/28/23

Point to the picture that matches the description.

1. The girl with the red hair is second.

2. The boy with the hat is first.

3. The girl with the black hair is third.

4. The girl with the black hair is first.

Which group shows the fish ordered from smallest to largest?

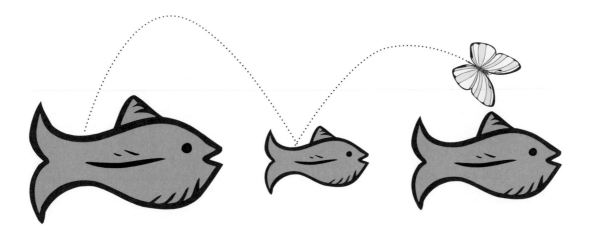

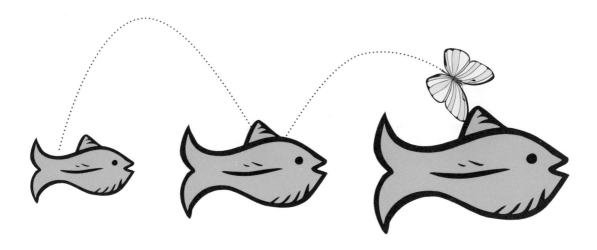

4/28/23

Use your fingers on one hand to show the number of bugs in each picture.

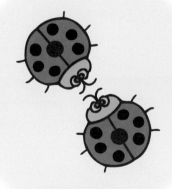

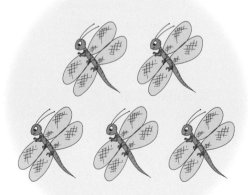

Triangles

1. Point to and count the sides of each triangle.
2. How many sides do triangles have?
3. Point to and count the corners of each triangle.
4. How many corners do triangles have?

4/28/23 (Justine)

Point to the triangles in each row.

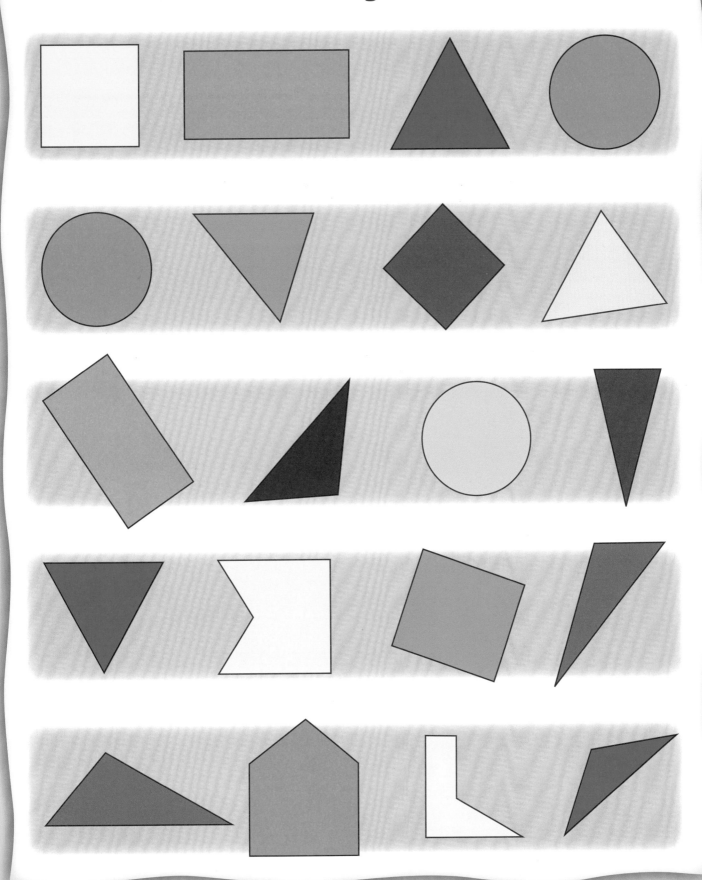

Rectangles

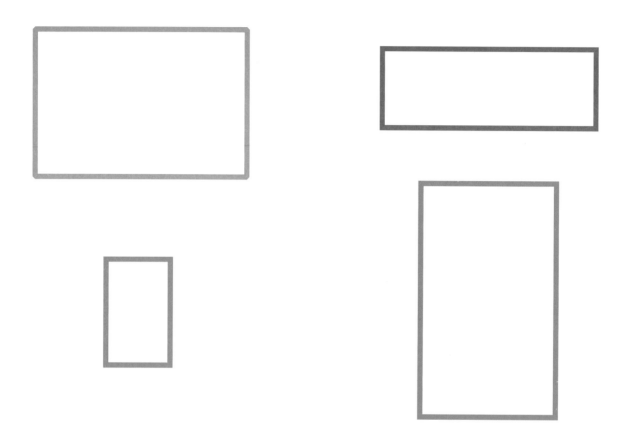

1. Point to each figure and say rectangle.

2. Count the sides of each rectangle.

3. How many sides do rectangles have?

4. Count the corners of each rectangle.

5. How many corners do all rectangles have?

Teaching note: As you travel, ask your child to point out rectangles to you.

Point to the rectangles in each row.

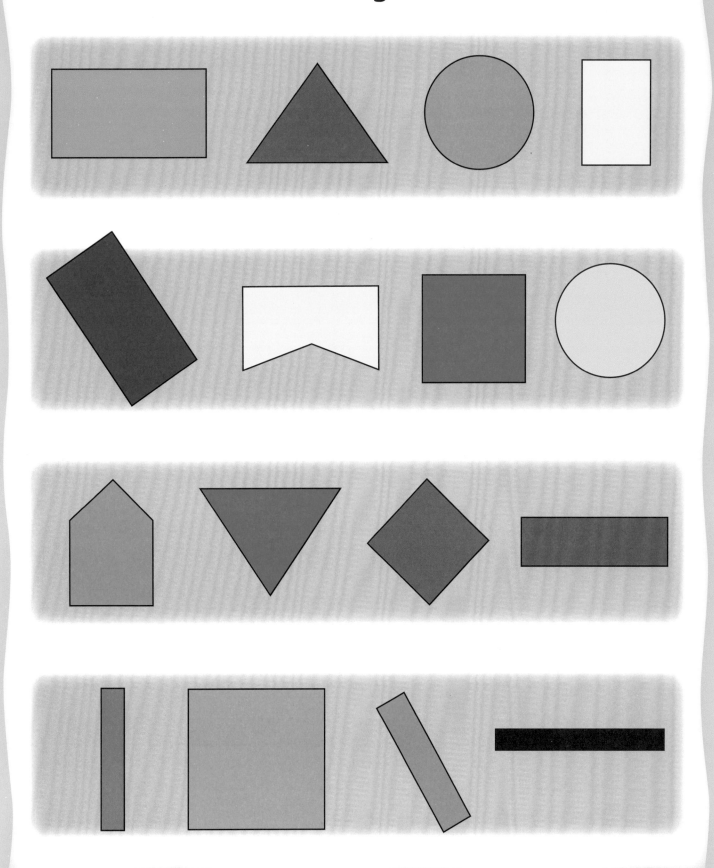

5/11/23 Justine

Squares

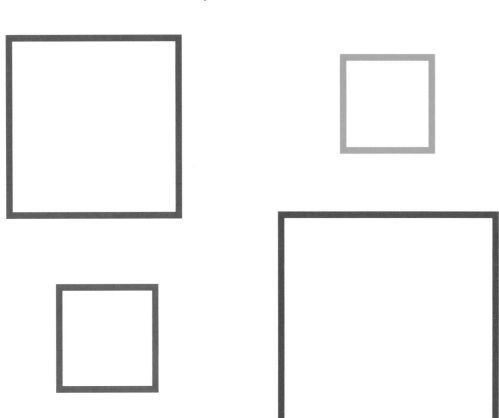

A square is a rectangle with 4 sides that are the same length.

1. Point to each figure and say square.

2. Count the sides of each square.

3. How many sides do squares have?

4. Count the corners of each square.

5. How many corners do all squares have?

Point to the squares in each row.

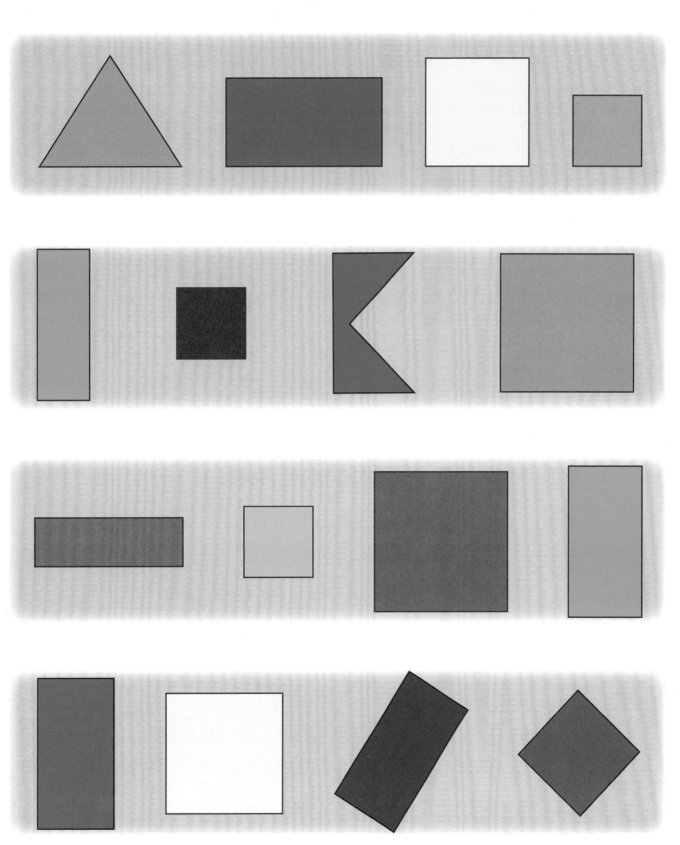

Point to the picture that matches the description.

1. There is a green dinosaur behind the boy.

2. There is a blue boat in front of the boy.

3. There are two dinosaurs beside the boy.

4. There is a red dinosaur behind the boy.

Point to the picture that matches the description.

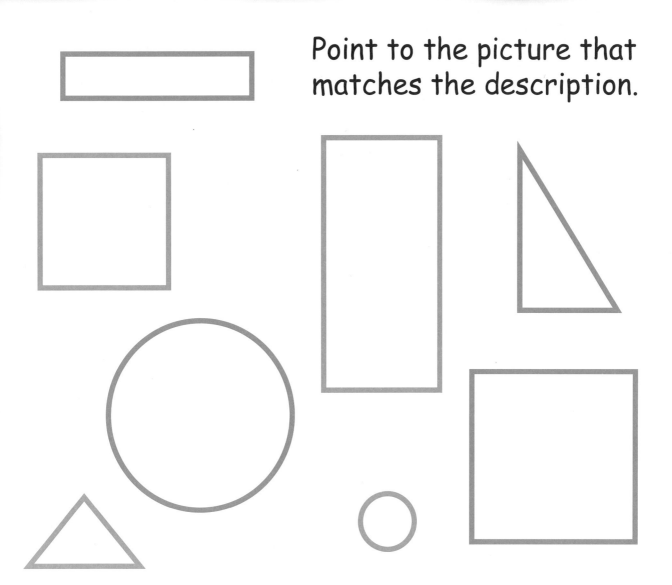

1. the blue circle

2. the green square

3. the green triangle

4. the big blue rectangle

5. the blue triangle

6. the green circle

7. the blue square

Point to the picture that matches the description.

1. The snail is first in line.

2. The turtle is third in line.

3. The turtle is second in line.

4. The snail is second in line.

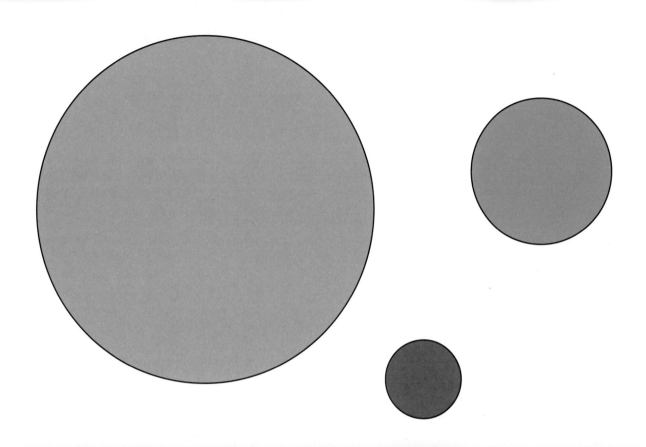

1. Which circle is the largest?

2. Which circle is the smallest?

3. Draw a line segment between the largest circle and the smallest circle.

4. Draw a line segment above the largest circle.

5. Draw a line segment under the green circle.

THINKER DOODLES™*

1. Look at each bug above, then find its unfinished picture below. Use a pencil to draw in all the missing parts.

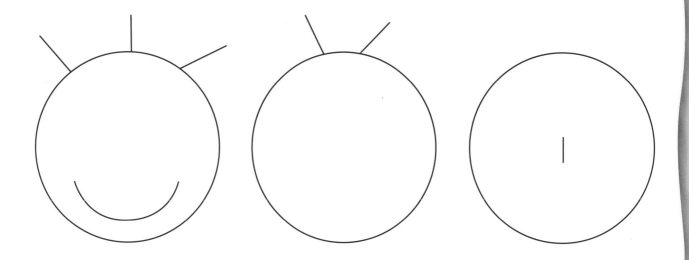

2. Draw eyebrows on the sad faces.
3. Give each of the other bugs two more hairs.

*For more activities like this, see our *Thinker Doodles*™ series.

How many umbrellas? Color 2 of them.

How many triangles? Color 5 of them.

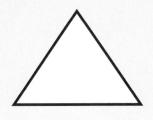 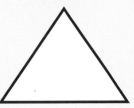 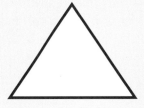

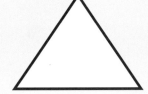 

CAN YOU FIND ME?™*

The race is on, I'm pretty fast.

I passed the tree, I'm not last.

My shorts are green, my shirt is blue.

Someone behind me stepped in goo.

Of the four runners that you see,

tell me now, can you find me?

*For more activities like this, see our *Can You Find Me?*™ series.

Count aloud the number of animals in each picture.

Count the numbers aloud.

Draw a line segment from each object to the picture of weather it is worn in.

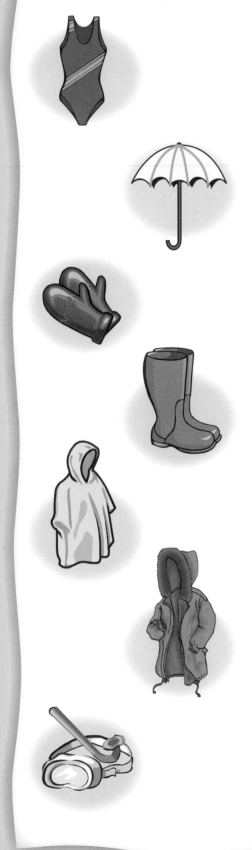

How many straight sides in a triangle?
Touch and count each side of each triangle.

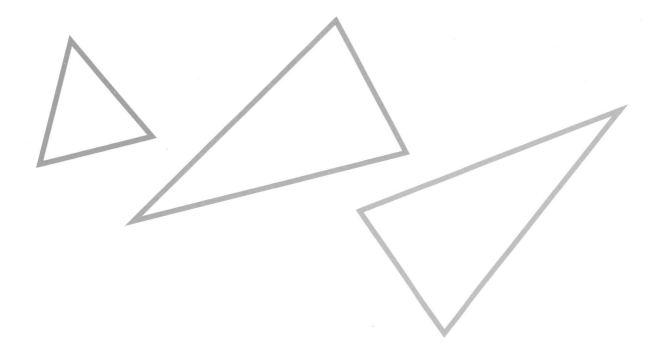

How many corners in a triangle?
Touch and count the corners of each triangle.

1. How many wheels are needed to finish the bikes below?

2. How many bikes like this one can be made from the wheels below?

3. How many wheels will be left over?

1

Touch and count the frogs in each picture.

2

3

4

5

THINKER DOODLES™*

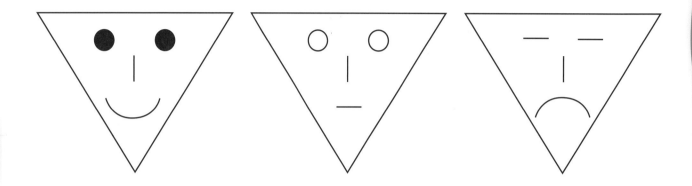

1. Look at each face above, then find its unfinished picture below. Use a pencil to draw all of the missing parts.

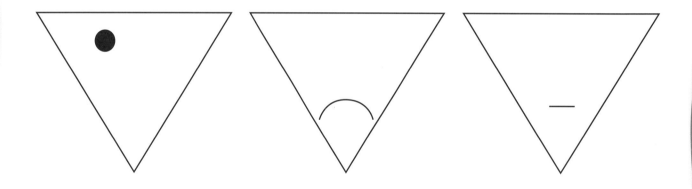

2. Color the faces with round eyes the same.
3. Color the sad faces differently than the other faces.

*For more activities like this, see our *Thinker Doodles*™ series.

Use the yellow ruler to answer the questions.

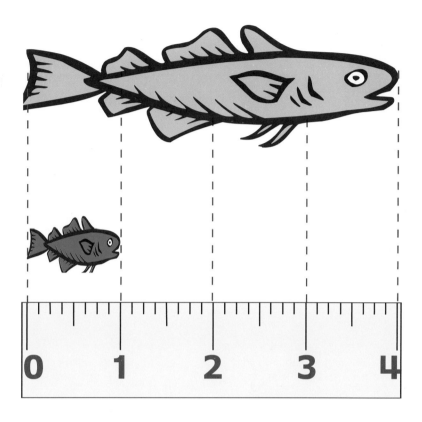

1. How many inches long is the red fish?

2. How many inches long is the blue fish?

3. Which fish is more than an inch long?

Draw a line segment to the matching quantities.

© 2009 The Critical Thinking Co.™ • www.CriticalThinking.com • 800-458-4849

Draw a line segment to the matching quantities.

1

2

3

4

5

1. Which picture has 3 shoes in it?

2. Which picture has 4 shoes in it?

3. Which picture has the fewest shoes in it?

4. Which picture has the most shoes in it?

Teaching Note: Using toys, cutting pictures from a storybook, or using magazine pictures could vary this activity. As your child is moving about the room, yard, or neighborhood, call attention to situations with two objects or three, and ask your child to describe them telling which is more, or fewer.

1 red apple

How many yellow apples?

How many red apples?

How many yellow apples?

How many red apples?

1. How many bugs are in the picture?

2. How many frogs are in the picture?

You can show there are the same number of things in groups by connecting things in one group with things in the other group.

3. Draw a line segment from each frog to a different bug.

4. Do you think frogs like to eat bugs?

CAN YOU FIND ME?*

The bike I ride is shiny and red,

but in the winter, I ride my sled.

Sometimes Dad lets me ride his horse,

I wear a helmet to be safe—of course.

Of the three pictures that you can see,

tell me now, can you find me?

*For more activities like this, see our *Can You Find Me?*™ series.

How many whales?
Color 4 whales.

How many cars?
Color 5 cars.

Hopping Rabbit

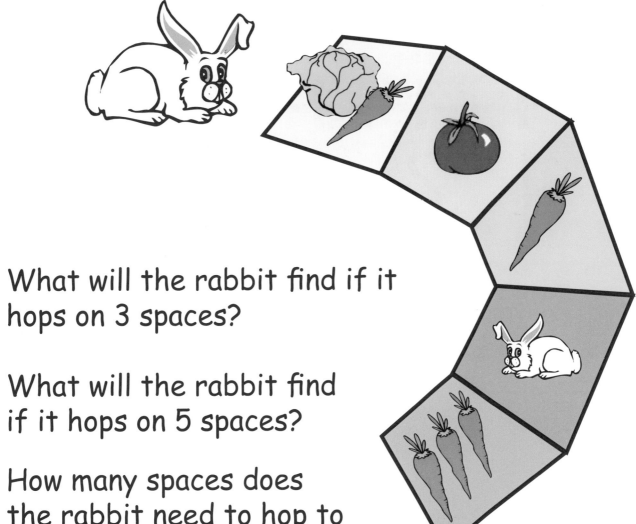

What will the rabbit find if it hops on 3 spaces?

What will the rabbit find if it hops on 5 spaces?

How many spaces does the rabbit need to hop to find lettuce and a carrot?

How many spaces does the rabbit need to hop to find a tomato?

How many spaces does the rabbit need to hop to find the baby rabbit?

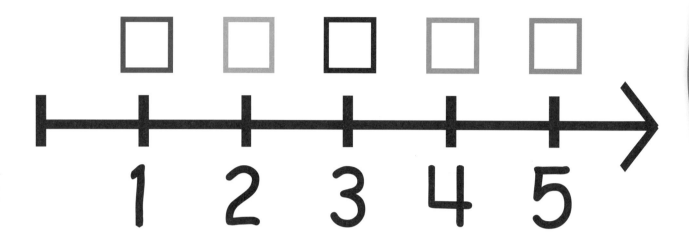

1. Point to the red square and say the numeral below it.

2. Point to the orange square and say the numeral below it.

3. Point to the blue square and say the numeral below it.

4. Point to the black square and say the numeral below it.

5. Point to the green square and say the numeral below it.

Draw a line segment to connect each numeral to the same number of dots.

1

2

3

4

5

Circle the groups with 5.
Put an X on the group with 4.

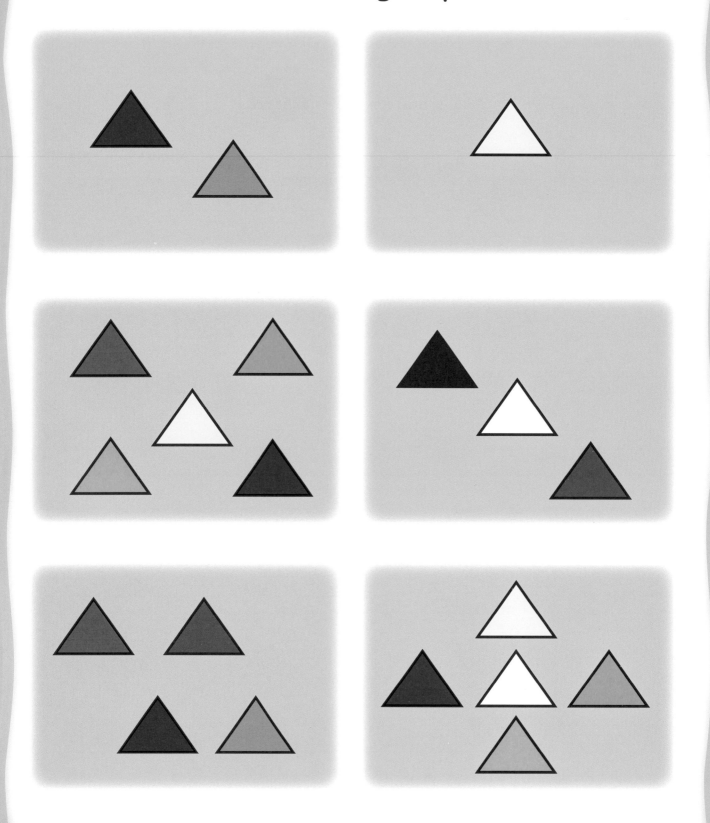

Point to the picture that matches the description.

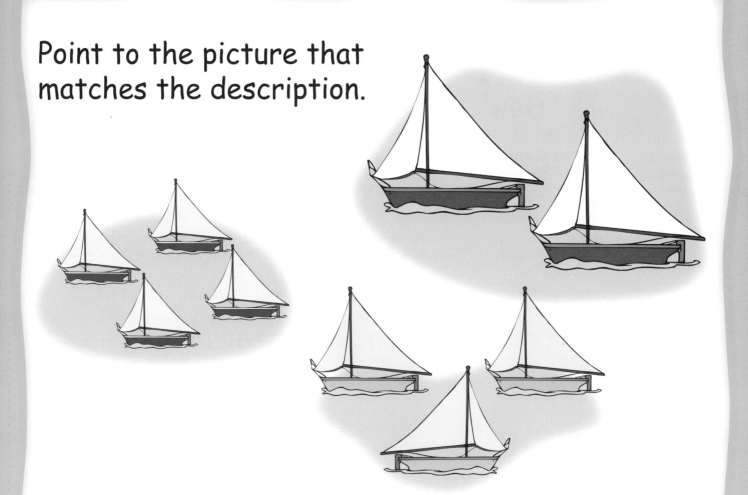

1. The picture of two sailboats.

2. The picture of three sailboats.

3. The picture of four sailboats.

4. The picture with the fewest sailboats.

5. The picture with the most sailboats.

6. The picture with the biggest sailboats.

7. The picture with the smallest sailboats.

How many stars are red?

Color more to make 4 stars red.

How many hens are brown?

Color more to make 5 hens brown.

Draw a line segment from each penguin to its lunch.

This penguin ate 2 fish.

This penguin ate 5 fish.

This penguin ate 1 fish.

This penguin ate 3 fish.

We can show that there is the same number of things in groups by connecting things in one group with things in the other group.

1. How many swings are in the picture?

2. How many children are in the picture?

3. Draw a line segment to connect each swing with a child.

Draw a line segment from each dog to its bones.

Red has 4 bones.
Spot has 3 bones.
Black has 2 bones.
Blue has 5 bones.

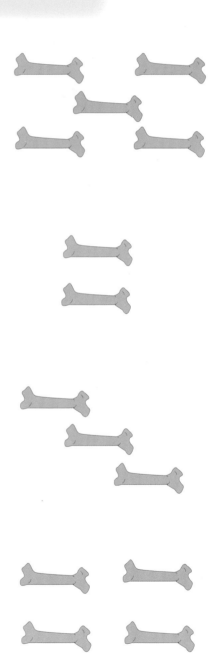

Which group of balloons is numbered correctly from 1 to 5?

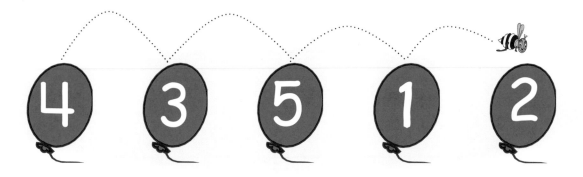

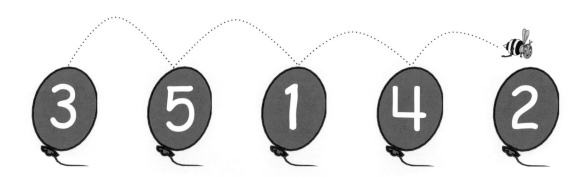

Point to each picture with five things in it.

   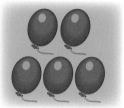

   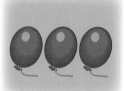

   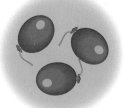

Draw a line segment to connect the dots by counting from 1 to 5.

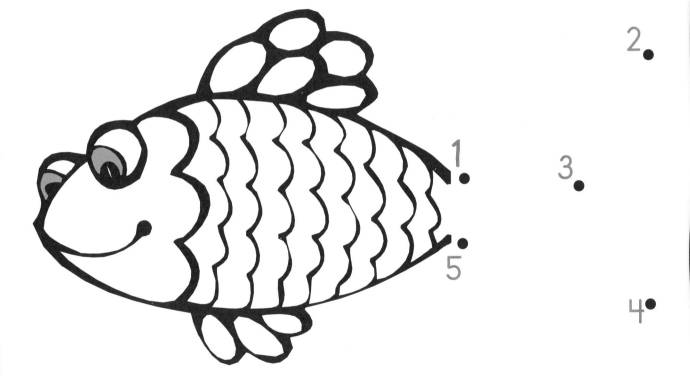

Draw 5 bubbles above the fish.

Point to the picture that matches the description.

1. The children are dressed for winter.

2. The children are dressed for summer.

3. The children are dressed for a special occasion.

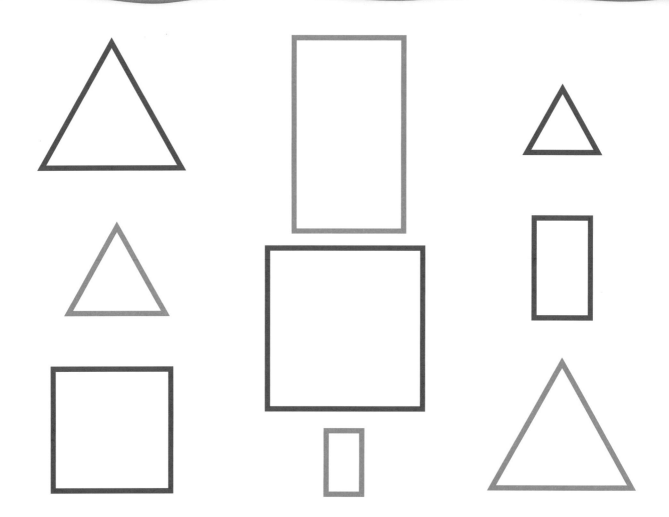

Point to the figure that matches the description.

1. the largest red square

2. the smallest green rectangle

3. the largest red triangle

4. the smallest red triangle

5. the smallest green triangle

6. the smallest red square

7. the largest green rectangle

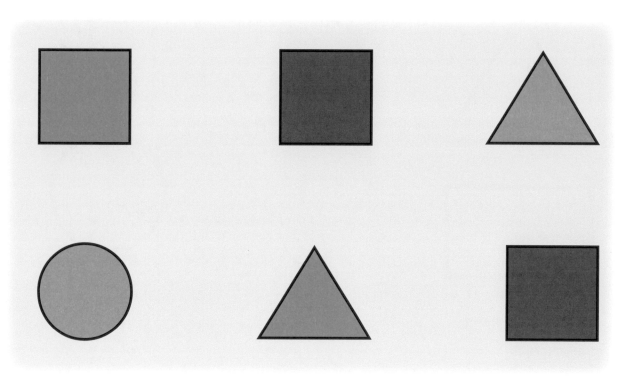

Color the shapes below so that the bottom group has the same colors as the top group.

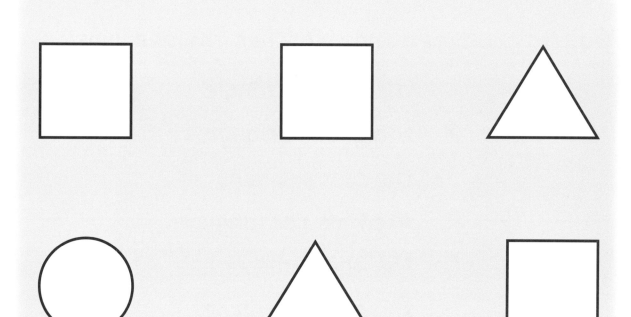

Point to the figure that matches the description.

1. the red rectangle

2. the green triangle

3. the black square

4. the blue rectangle

5. the green circle

6. the black triangle

7. the green square

Which mother cat has the most kittens?
Which mother cat has the fewest kittens?

Which tree has the fewest apples?
Which tree has the most apples?

CAN YOU FIND ME?*

My pattern you'll see,

is one square, then three.

The first square is red, the next are blue.

What does this pattern look like to you?

Of the three pictures that you see,

tell me now, can you find me?

*For more activities like this, see our *Can You Find Me?*™ series.

1. Point to the person who is second in line and say the color of his or her clothes.

2. Point to the person who is first in line and say the color of his or her clothes.

3. Point to the person who is third in line and say the color of his or her clothes.

Point to the figure that matches the description.

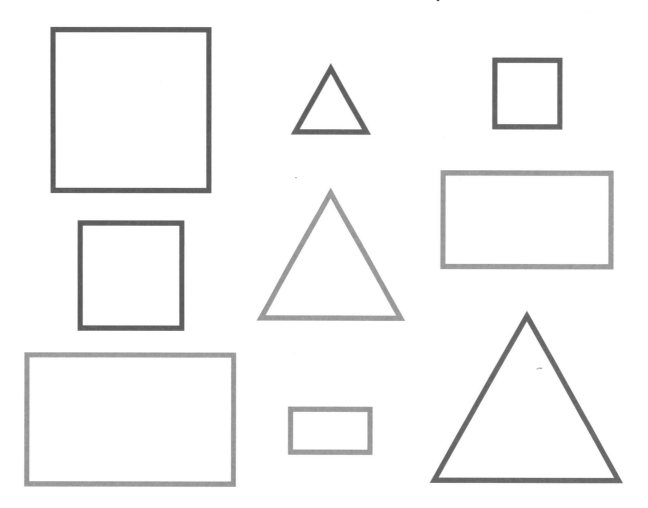

1. the largest blue rectangle

2. the smallest red square

3. the largest red square

4. the smallest blue rectangle

5. the smallest triangle

6. the largest triangle

Which person is tallest?
Which person is shortest?

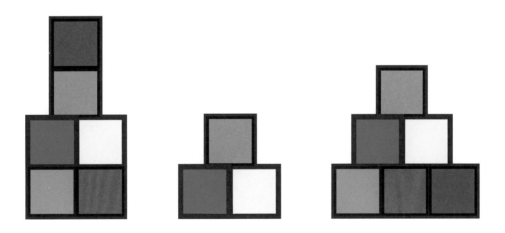

Which block stack is tallest?
Which block stack is shortest?

Point to each object and say its shape and color.

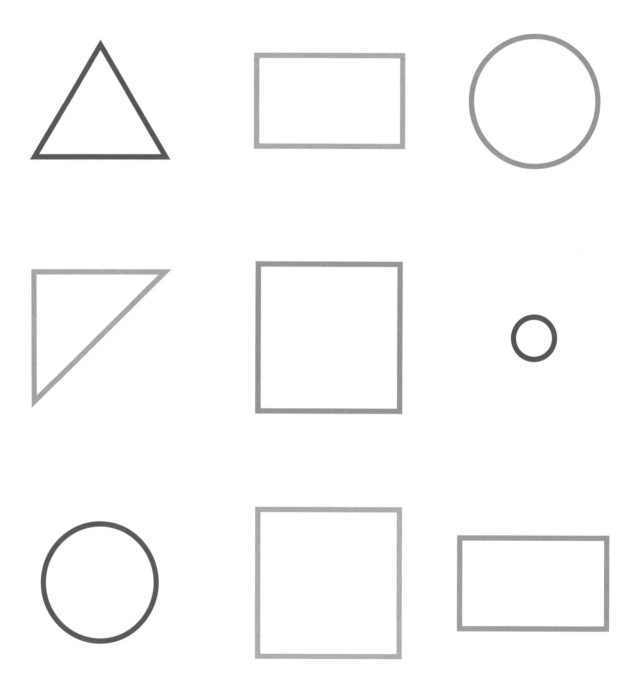

Point to the object in each group with the most corners and say its shape.

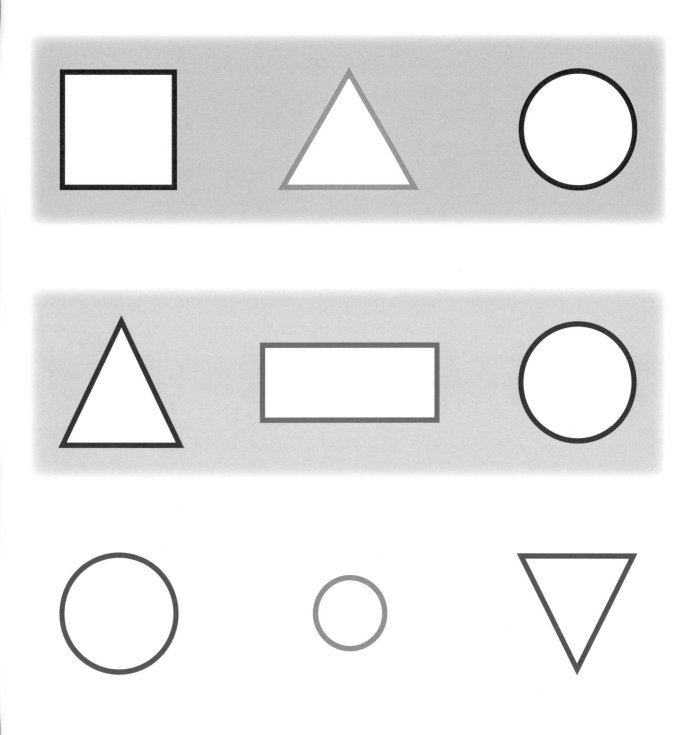

Teaching Note: A square is also a rectangle so either answer is acceptable.

Touch and say the name of each item in the pattern. Then say the name of the object behind the green curtain that will continue the pattern.

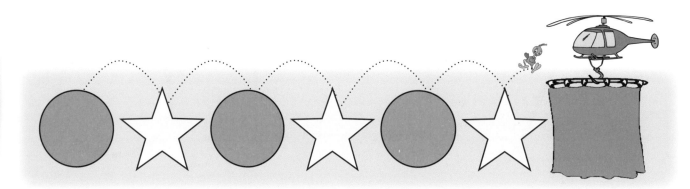

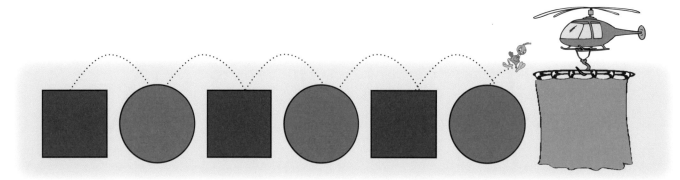

Draw line segments to match the numerals and fingers.

1

2

3

4

5

CAN YOU FIND ME?*

I'm one of five frogs,
perched on a log.
We are all in a line,
enjoying sunshine.

My sister's up front.
My brother in the back.
I'm not third or fourth,
and my name is Zack.

Of the 5 frogs that you see,
tell me now, can you find me?

*For more activities like this, see our *Can You Find Me?*™ series.

Touch and say the name of each item in the pattern. Then say the name of the object behind the green curtain that will continue the pattern.

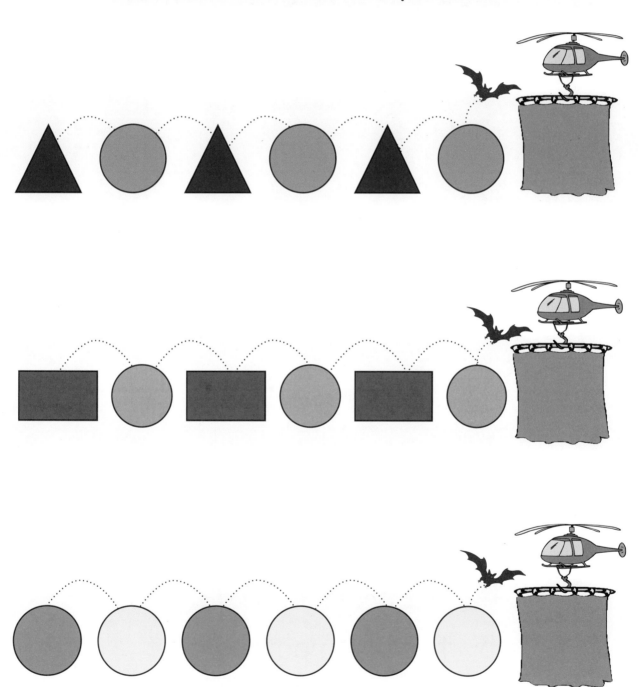

Point to the object that matches the description.

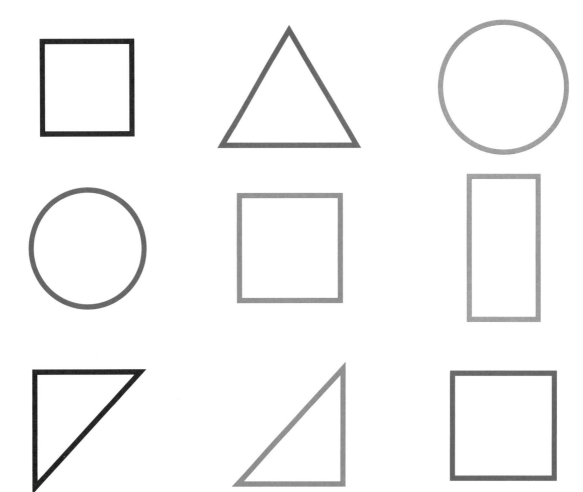

1. the green square

2. the red triangle

3. the blue circle

4. the green triangle

5. the blue rectangle

6. the red square

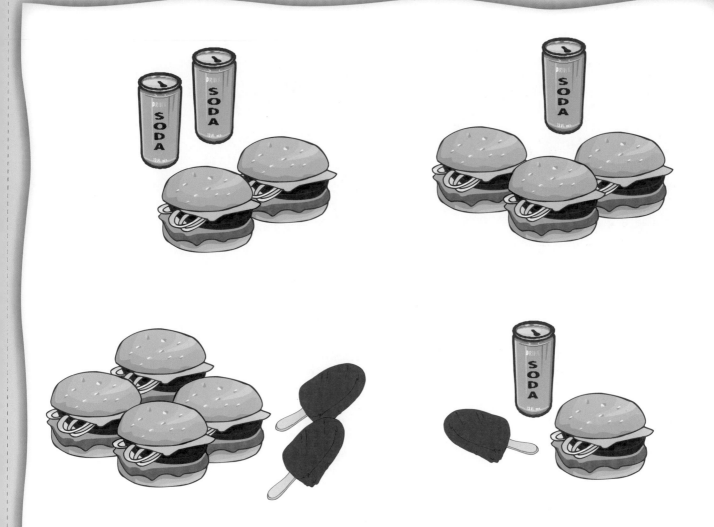

1. Point to the picture with 3 burgers and 1 soda.

2. Point to the picture with 4 burgers and
    2 ice cream bars.

3. Point to the picture with 2 burgers and
    2 sodas.

4. Point to the picture with 1 burger, 1 ice cream
    bar, and 1 soda.

5. Point to the picture with the most burgers.

Each student brought a favorite stuffed animal to school. Count the pictures to answer the questions.

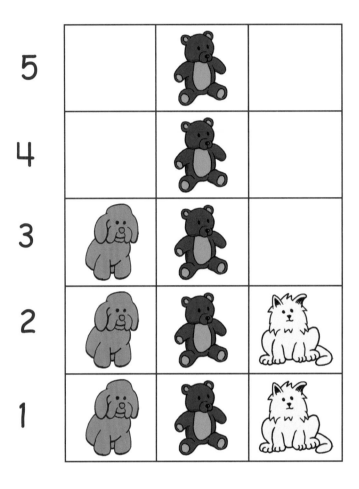

1. How many dogs are there?

2. What animal group has less than three?

3. How many more bears are there than dogs?

Touch and count the pictures in each group.

balloons	
stars	
bears	
fish	
apples	
frogs	
clowns	

Look at the other page to answer the questions.

How many stars?
How many bears?
Which is more?

How many fish?
How many frogs?
Which is more?

How many apples?
How many fish?
Which is more?

How many clowns?
How many bears?
Which is more?

Point to the figure that matches the description.

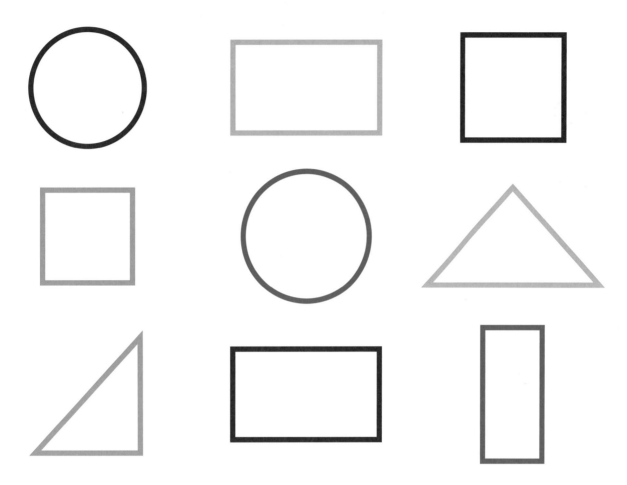

1. the red circle

2. the blue rectangle

3. the green square

4. the blue triangle

5. the black square

6. the red rectangle

7. the green triangle

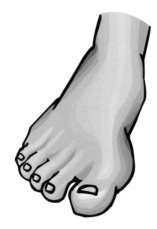

Toe Counting Song

Touch your toes for each verse, beginning with the big toe.

This little piggy went to market;

This little piggy stayed home;

This little piggy had roast beef;

This little piggy had none;

This little piggy cried,

"Wee, wee, wee!" all the way home!

1 2 3 4 5

How many toes did we count?

Draw a line segment to connect each dog to its birthday biscuit.

This dog is 3 years old.

This dog is 5 years old.

This dog is a year older than the youngest dog.

Count aloud, then point to the correct number.

This is Anna's birthday cake.

How old is she now?

1   2   3   4   5

Draw the candles Anna will need next year.

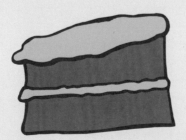

How old will she be then?

Point to the longer rectangle in each set of rectangles.

Which box is the biggest?

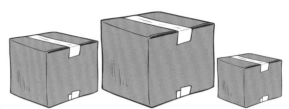

Which box is the smallest?

Which tree is the tallest?

Which tree is the shortest?

Which worm is the longest?

Which worm is the shortest?

Use your fingers on one hand to count how many animals are in each picture.

1. What is under the umbrella?

2. What is beside the sand castle?

3. Draw a ball ⬤ in front of the sand castle.

4. Draw a ball ⬤ between the umbrella and towel.

Touch each figure and say its color and shape.

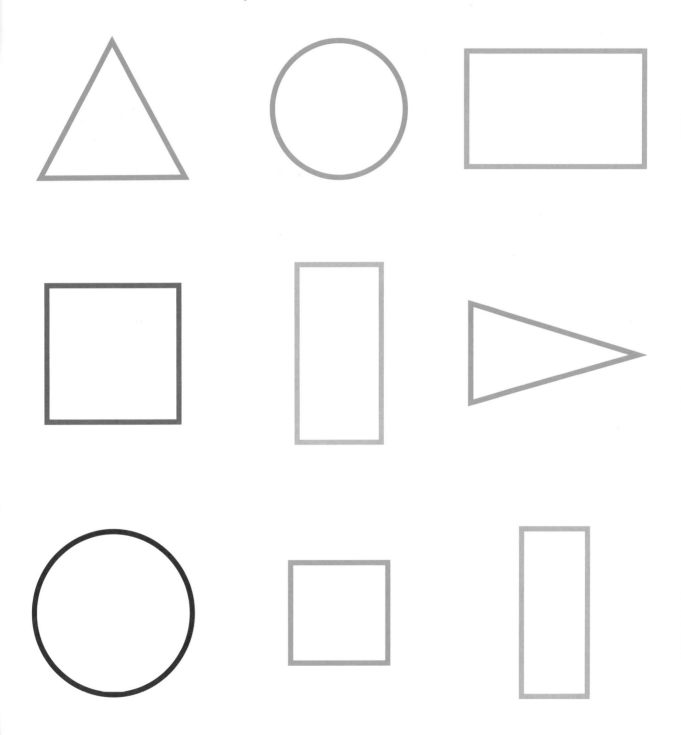

Teaching Note: Have your child identify squares as squares, although they are also rectangles.

1. How many brown horses are in the picture?

2. How many white horses are in the picture?

3. How many black horses are in the picture?

4. How many horses altogether in the picture?

5. Are there more black horses or white horses in the picture?

6. If you ride one horse away, how many horses are left?

1. Point to the green shape and say its name.

2. Point to the blue shape and say its name.

3. Point to the red shape and say its name.

4. Point to the orange shape and say its name.

5. How many shapes is the clown juggling?

6. How many different colors are the shapes?

7. If the clown drops a shape, how many would be left?

1. How many yellow fish are in the fish tank?

2. How many red fish are in the fish tank?

3. How many blue fish are in the fish tank?

4. What color is the biggest fish in the fish tank?

5. How many fish altogether in the fish tank?

6. Are there more red fish or blue fish in the fish tank?

7. If one fish is moved to another fish tank, how many fish are left?

1. Which shape has the most straight sides?

2. How many straight sides does it have?

3. Which shape has the most corners?

4. How many corners does it have?

5. Which shape has the fewest straight sides?

6. How many straight sides does it have?

7. How many corners does it have?

8. What figure has three corners?

9. How many straight sides does the triangle have?

How many triangles are in each group?

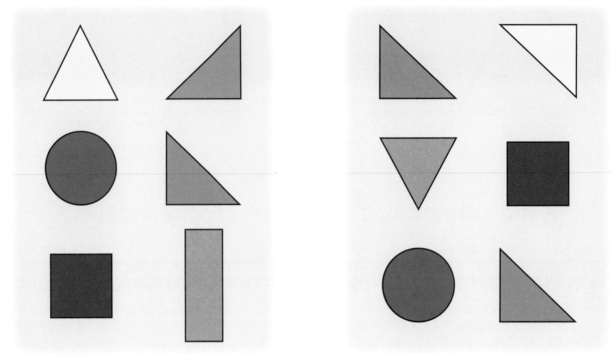

How many circles are in each group?

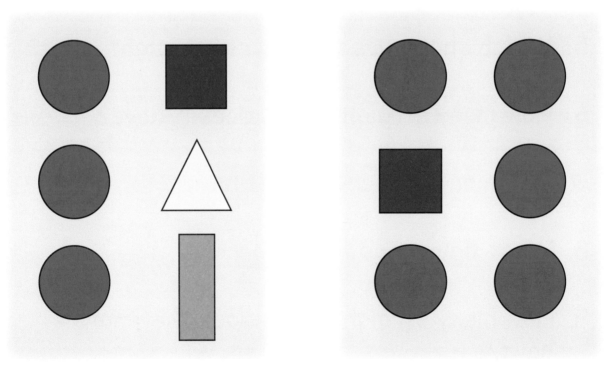

1. How many circles are in the picture?

2. How many squares are in the picture?

3. How many triangles are in the picture?

4. Are there more squares or triangles in the picture?

5. What is the largest shape in the picture?

Teaching Note: Five circles counting snowman's eyes. Four squares (3 stepping blocks and dog house). Two triangles (snowman's hat and roof of dog house).

Touch and say the name of each item in the pattern. Then say the name of the object behind the green curtain that will continue the pattern.

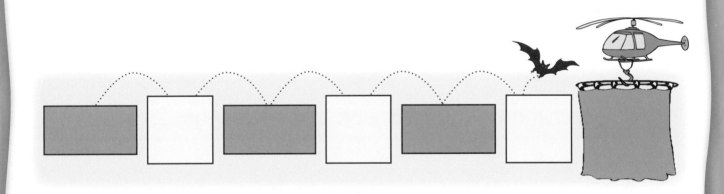

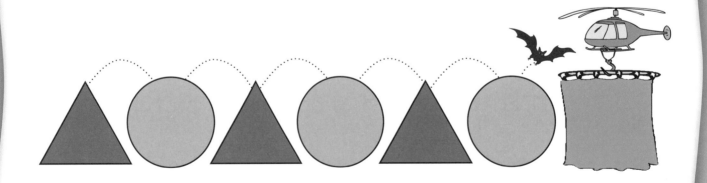

Rectangles
Point to the rectangle in each group and say its name and color.

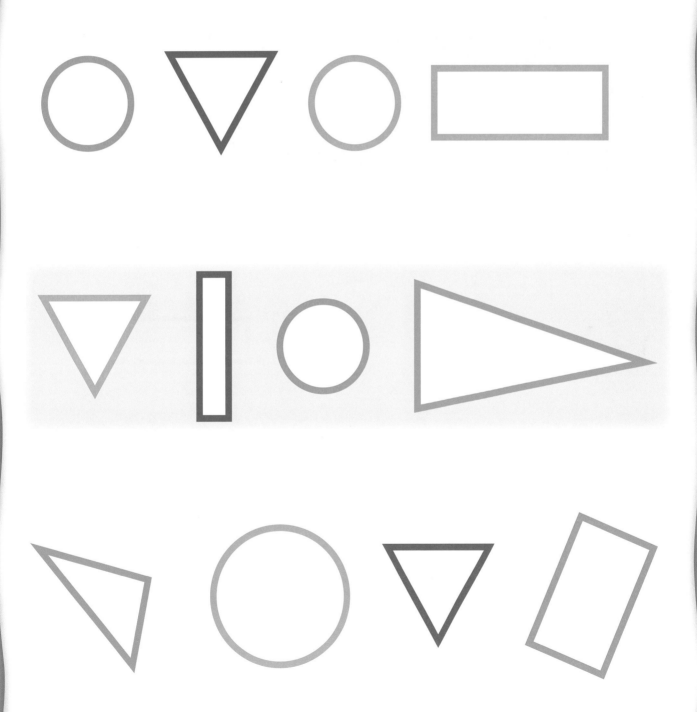

Point to the object in each group with the most corners and say its shape and how many corners it has.

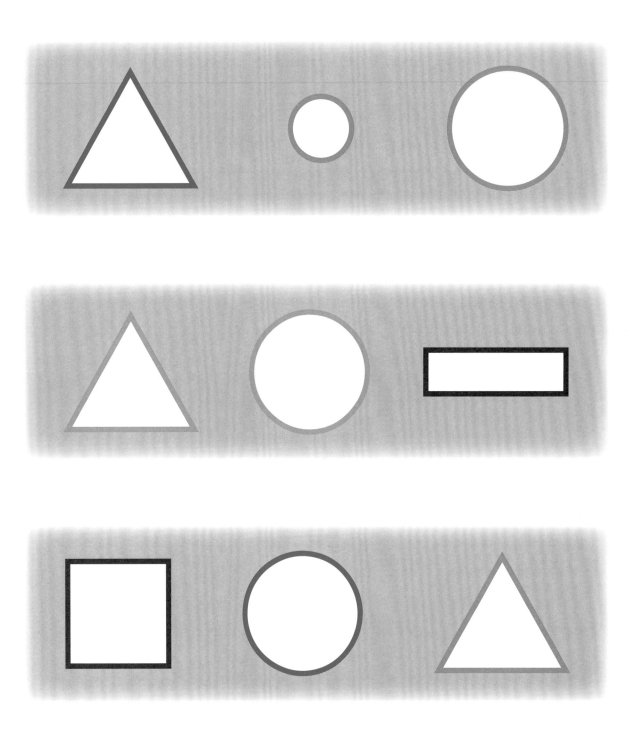

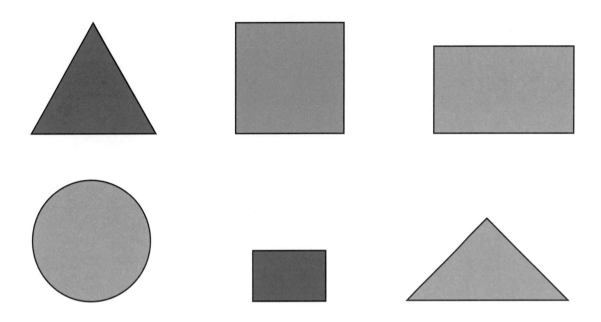

1. How many triangles are in the picture?

2. How many red figures are in the picture?

3. How many squares are in the picture?

4. How many circles are in the picture?

5. Are there more red figures or blue figures in the picture?

6. How many rectangles are in the picture?

Teaching Note: If necessary, remind your child that squares are rectangles.

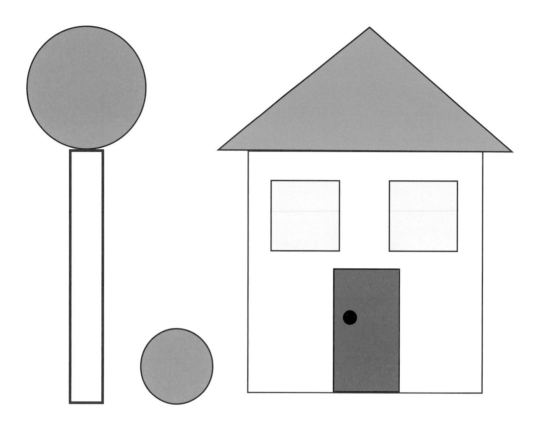

Find the shapes in the picture.

one triangle
three circles
three squares
five rectangles

Teaching Note: If necessary, remind your child that a square is a special type of rectangle.

Use your fingers on one hand to show how many lizards are in each group.

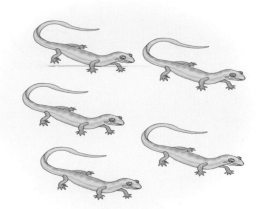

Put an X over the one that doesn't belong. Explain why the object does not belong.

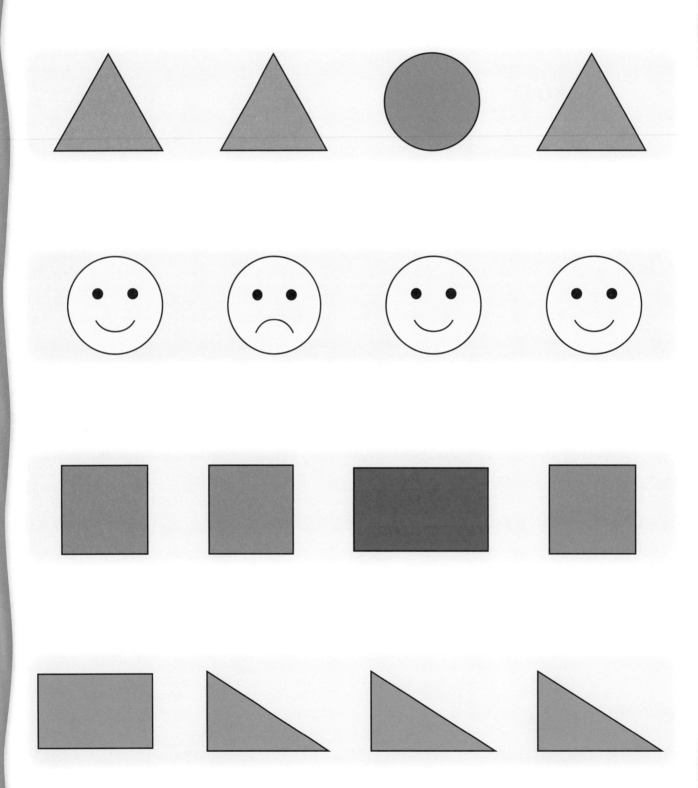

Use your fingers on one hand to show the total of both groups.

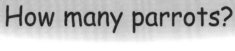

How many parrots?

How many snakes?

How many rats?

1. What animal is the first in line to swim in the water?

2. What animal is the third in line to swim in the water?

3. What animal is the fifth in line to swim in the water?

4. What animal is the second in line to swim in the water?

5. What animal is the fourth in line to swim in the water?

Touch and count the balls.
Touch and say the numbers.

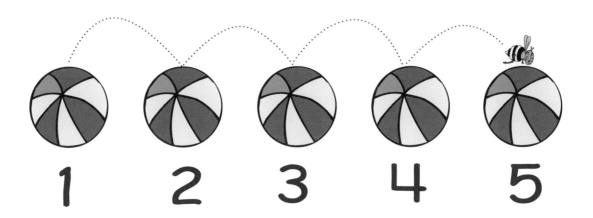

Point to the group of balloons that is numbered in order from 1 to 5.

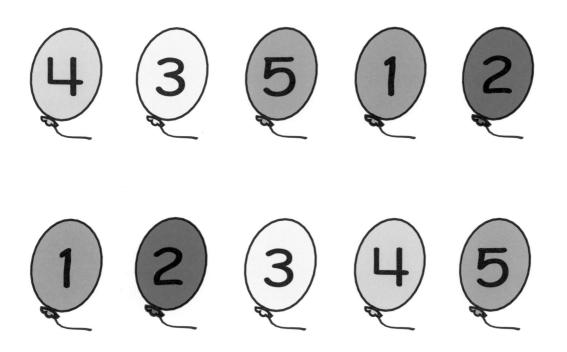

1. Which group is in shortest to tallest order?
2. Which group is in tallest to shortest order?

THINKER DOODLES™*

1. Look at each face above, then find its unfinished picture below. Use a pencil to draw all the missing parts.

2. Color the faces with hair red.
3. Color the remaining faces blue.

*For more activities like this, see our *Thinker Doodles*™ series.

1. Point to the stool that has one toy above it.

2. Point to the stool that has two toys above it.

3. Point to the stool that has three toys above it.

4. Point to the stool that has four toys above it.

5. Point to the stool that has the fewest toys.

6. Point to the stool that has the most toys.

Point to the object that does not belong. Explain why it doesn't belong in the group.

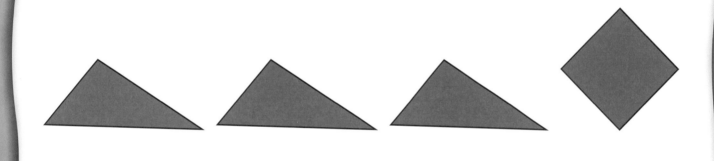

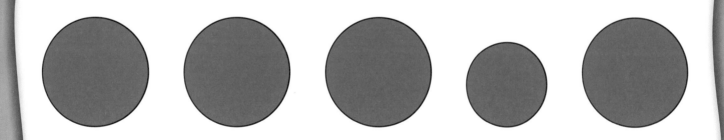

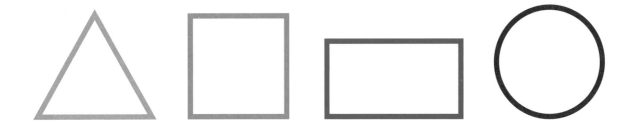

1. Say the name of the two shapes with the same number of sides.

2. Say the name of the two shapes with the same number of corners.

3. Which shape has three sides?

4. Which shape has three corners?

5. Draw a shape below with four sides and four corners.

1. Point to the group that is in the smallest to largest order.

2. Which group is in the largest to smallest order?

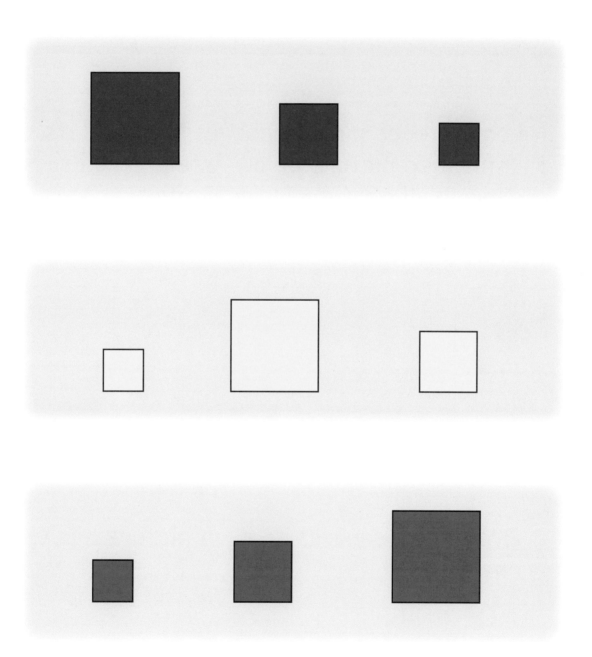

THINKER DOODLES™*

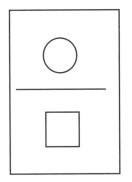 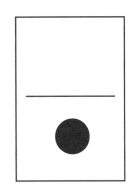 

1. Look at each picture above, then find its unfinished picture below. Use a pencil to draw in all of the missing parts.

 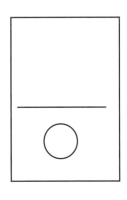 

2. Draw more squares so each picture has one square.

*For more activities like this, see our *Thinker Doodles*™ series.

Use your fingers on one hand to count the total number of both groups.

How many owls?

How many cats?

How many butterflies?

Point to and say the names of the two shapes that are the same in each group.

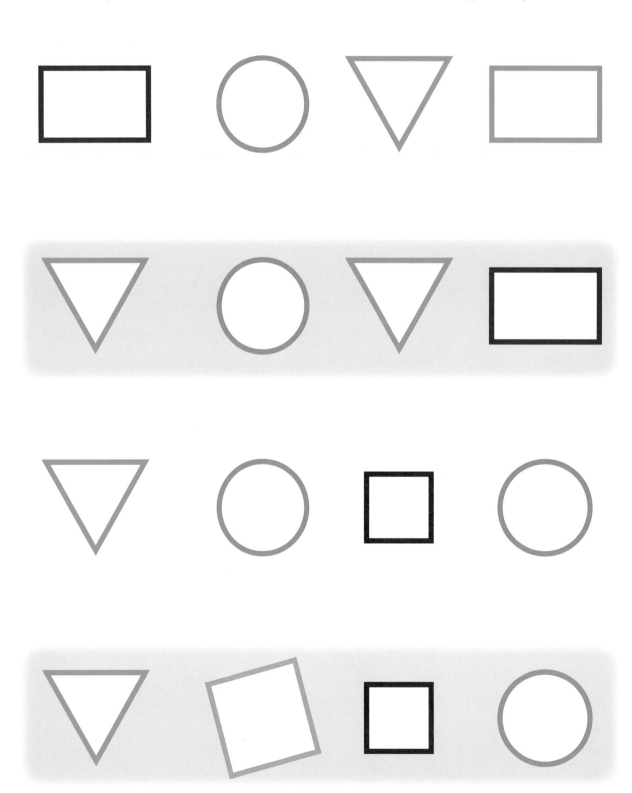

Point to the group with the most things in it.
Then point to the group with the fewest things in it.

Draw a line segment from each child to his or her candy.

Deb has the most
red candy.

Megan has the least
yellow candy.

Tim has less candy
than Deb.

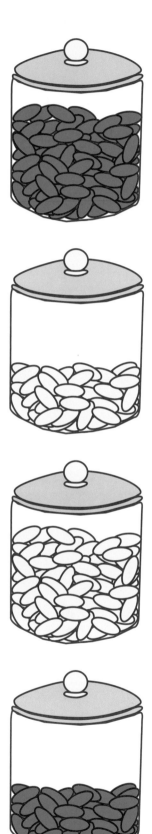

Count the stars, then point to and say the number.

Put an X on the red star.

Point to and say the number of stars left.

1 2 3 4 5

How many squares?

Put an X on the blue and green squares.

Point to and say the number of squares left.

1 2 3 4 5

Count the dogs, then point to
and say the number.

Put an X over the brown and yellow dogs.
Point to and say the number of dogs left.

1   2   3   4   5

How many balloons?

Put an X over the balloon with the shortest string.
Point to and say the number of balloons left.

1   2   3   4   5

Tell how many blue boxes
will fit in each red box.

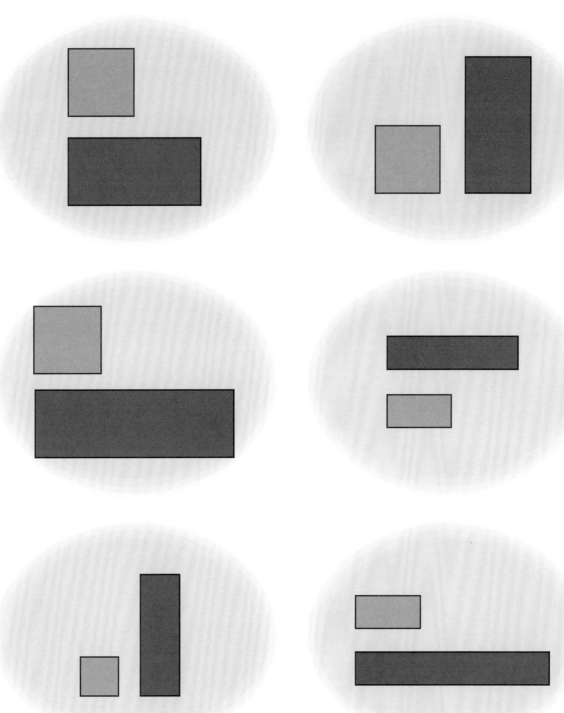

1. Which colored ball will drop in the water first?

2. Which colored ball will drop in the water third?

3. Which colored ball will drop in the water second?

4. Which colored ball will drop in the water fifth?

5. Which colored ball will drop in the water fourth?

Count the bugs, then point to and say the number.

Put an X on the red and gray bugs.

Point to and say the number of bugs left.

1 2 3 4 5

How many fish?

Put an X over the green and red fish.

Point to and say the number of fish left.

1 2 3 4 5

1. Point to the tallest object in each set of pictures and say tallest.

2. Point to the shortest object in each set of pictures and say shortest.

1. Point to the group that is in the smallest to largest order.

2. Which group is in the largest to smallest order?

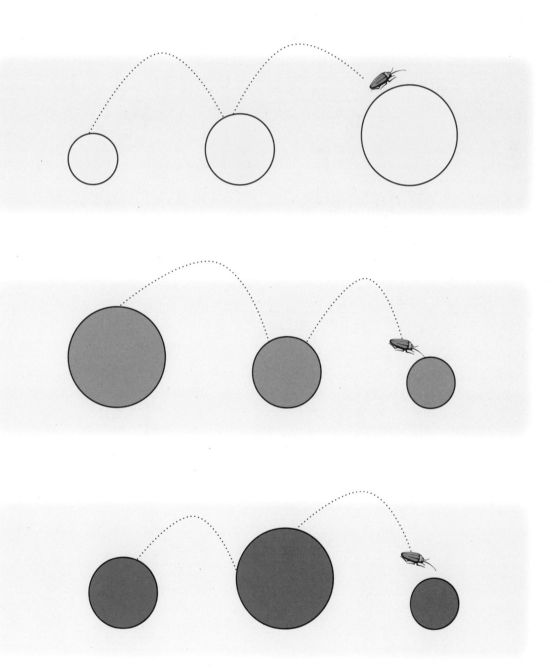

Point to the faster object in each set of pictures.

1. How many flowers are in the vase?

2. How many flowers are outside the vase?

3. Is the man outside or inside the house?

4. Is the cat outside or inside the house?

5. Is the clock above or below the window?

6. Is the cat above or below the table?

7. Is the book on or in the table?

Find each of the shapes in the picture below.

- 4 Triangles
- 3 Circles
- 3 Squares
- 2 Rectangles

1. Point to the column in each picture with the most things in it and say most.

2. Point to the group with the fewest things in each picture and say fewest.

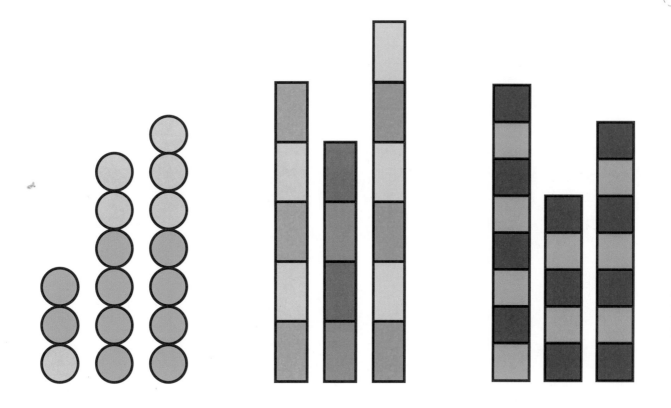

1. There were this many pennies inside my bank, but I lost two pennies.

Put an **X** over 2 pennies.

How many pennies are left in my bank?

1 2 3 4 5

2. There were this many gumballs in my pocket, but I lost 3 gumballs.

Put an **X** over 3 gumballs.

How many gumballs are left inside my pocket?

1 2 3 4 5

1. There were this many
   fish inside my fish tank,
   but my cat ate two fish.

   Put an X over 2 fish.

   How many fish are left in the tank?

   1   2   3   4   5

2. There were this many
   dogs in our yard, but
   four dogs left.

   Put an X over 4 dogs.

   How many dogs are left in the yard?

   1   2   3   4   5

1. How many birds are on the cat?

2. If one bird flew away, how many birds would be left on the cat?

1   2   3   4   5

1. How many apples are on the tree?

2. If two apples fell to the ground, how many apples would be left on the tree?

1   2   3   4   5

CAN YOU FIND ME?*

I started with five,

but now I have two.

Some are lost,

two is too few!

Of the pictures that you see, which birds are mine?
Please help me.

*For more activities like this, see our *Can You Find Me?*™ series.

Draw a line segment to show how you would share half of the food in each picture.

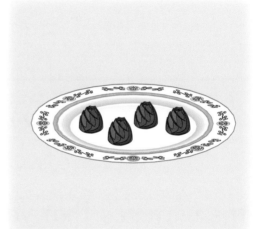

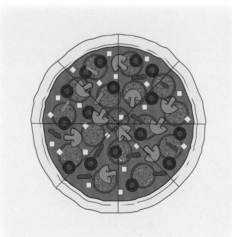

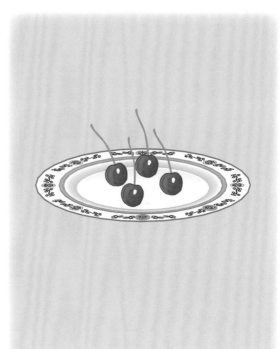

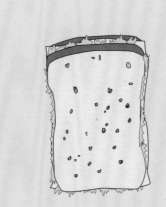

Tell how you would use color or shape to split each group into two groups.

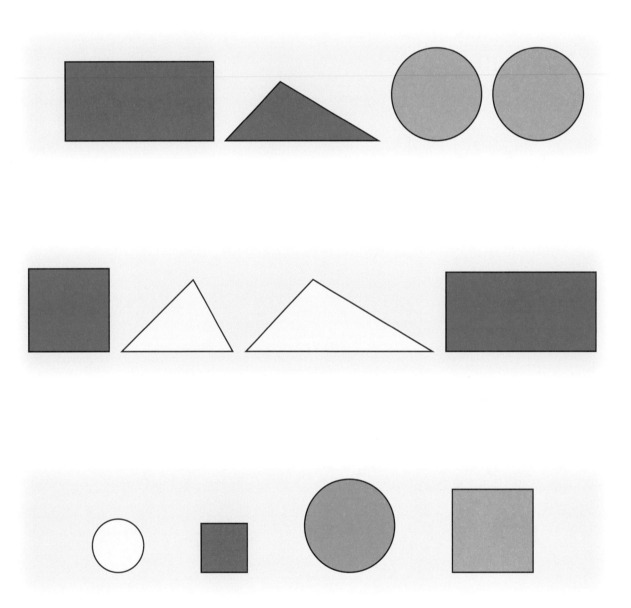

Teaching Note: There is no right answer. Your child could group by color, by shape, by objects that have corners, objects that do not have sharp corners, large and small, and so on. Any rational answer is acceptable provided your child can explain it.

CAN YOU FIND ME?*

If there were one more,
you would have four.
If you like things sweet,
you'll love me as a treat.

Of the pictures that you see,
point to the one that is me.

*For more activities like this, see our *Can You Find Me?*™ series.

1. How many triangles are in the picture?

2. How many circles are in the picture?

3. How many squares are in the picture?

4. How many rectangles are in the picture?

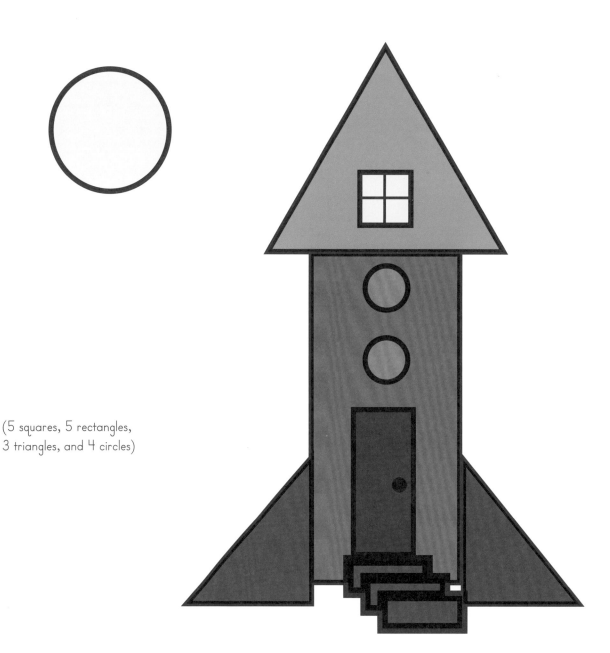

(5 squares, 5 rectangles,
3 triangles, and 4 circles)

Name the shapes in each group. Then point to the two shapes that are the same in each group.

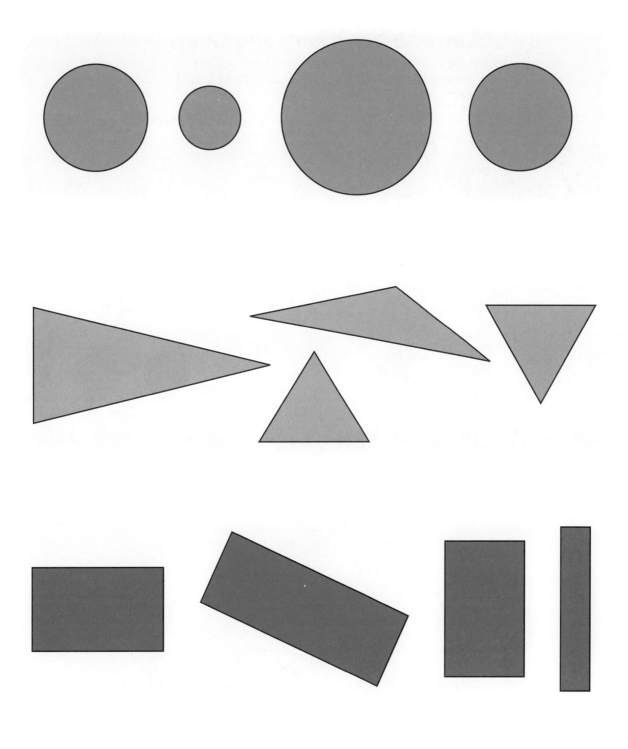

CAN YOU FIND ME?*

Sue has more than Tom,

but Tom has more than John.

Point to each picture below,

and tell me the name, if you know.

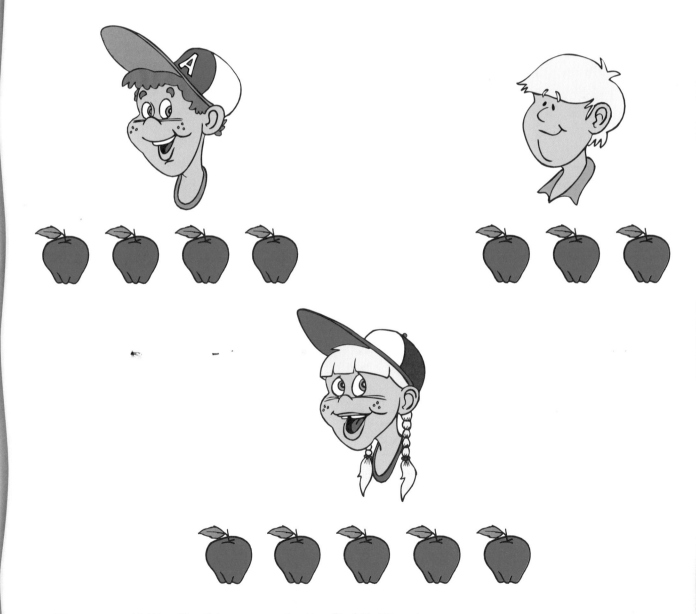

*For more activities like this, see our *Can You Find Me?*™ series.

234

© 2009 The Critical Thinking Co.™ • www.CriticalThinking.com • 800-458-4849

Circle the way you think the cup will land if it is dropped to the floor.

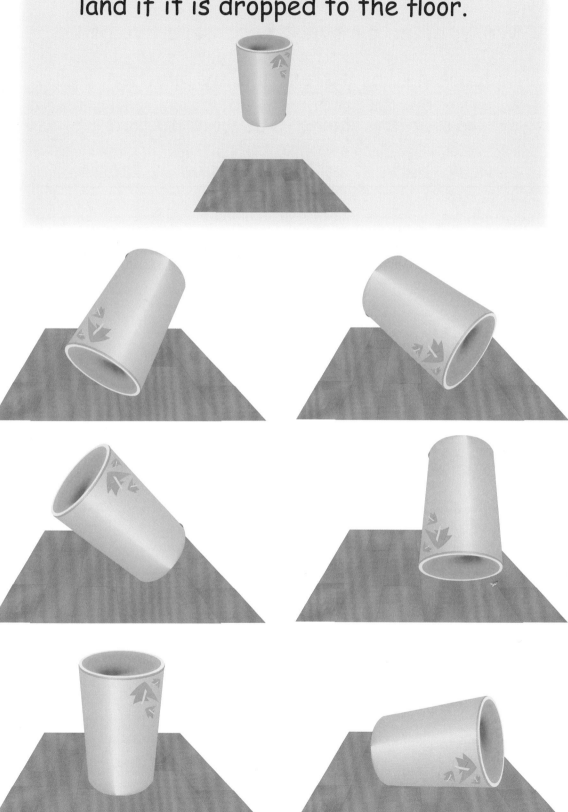

CAN YOU FIND ME?*

We watched a movie, there were five of us.

My parents, my sister, and my brother, Gus.

After the movie, Gus went to bed,

but the rest of us stayed up instead.

The rest of us are here below,

where are we, do you know?

*For more activities like this, see our Can You Find Me??™ series.